FORGOTTEN FAITH

-

A Streetwalkers Journey Back

NOTE:

"... in a Sep. 26, 2016 article on its website titled "Prostitution Statistics: What You Need to Know," wrote:

"According to Foundation Scelles, as reported in Le Figaro: Worldwide there is an estimation of 40-42 million prostitutes.

- 80 percent of the world population of prostitutes are female and range in age between 13-25.
- 90 percent of all prostitutes are dependent on a pimp.

While these statistics about prostitution are just touching the surface, they indicate the extent of the sex-for-sale industry worldwide.

There are an estimated 1-2 million prostitutes in the United States..."

(ProCon.org. (2018, January 11). How Many Prostitutes Are in the United States and the Rest of the World? Retrieved from http://prostitution.procon.org/view.answers.php?questionID=000095)

"The average age a teen enters the sex trade in the US is 12 to 14 years old. Many victims are runaway girls who were sexually abused as children." ("11 Facts About Human Trafficking." DoSomething.org Accessed Feb 7, 2020, https://www.dosomething.org/us/facts/11-facts-about-human-trafficking)

While there are some statistics that can be found, they are typically educated guesses many times using arrest records at the time. Consequently, it is impossible to give a correct census with accurate accompanying data.

Example: according to Linda Lowen;

"A 1991 study [130 San Francisco prostitutes] by the Council for Prostitution Alternatives, in Portland, Oregon, documented that 78 percent of 55 prostituted women reported being raped an average of 16 times annually by their pimps and 33 times a year by johns."

(https://www.thoughtco.com/prostitution-statistics-rape-physical-abuse-3534139)

It is hard to imagine the pain these girls go through unless you walk in her shoes, especially when she hears how many people believe; "If she wants to leave, she should just leave. If she does not leave, it is because she likes all the sex", "The prostitute deserves what she gets," or "Prostitution is a victimless crime".

It was one of the coldest winters in Bensenville's history, a small suburb of Chicago close to O'Hare airport. Well, at least it felt like the coldest winter to me each day as I made my way to my waitressing job in 1979 that I met Kim. A quiet young lady with a severe case of paranoia. I wondered why, what had happened to make her so afraid, but I did not ask. It was none of my business.

She frequented the small café and over the next few years, we became friends. It was not until 1982 that she told me a secret she had been keeping. I was fascinated and wanted to tell her story, but she just could not do that quite yet. She did, however, promise to let me know when she was ready to tell it to those who had an ear and true curiosity for the truth.

In 2018, she hunted me down and asked if I was still interested in telling her story. I was, provided nothing was embellished or exaggerated. Kim had her own demands and that was her story was to inform not glamorized or distract from the absolute truth. Her experiences were to remain as true as they were when she experienced them.

She was 62 years old when we last spoke!

In memory of Kim

1957 - 2019

"... "Never will I leave you, never will I forsake you."
Hebrews 13:5b

PART I

"When I was a child, I trusted and believed in the goodness of people. I trusted the police, doctors, and friends when I needed help. I also believed God was there, all around, loving us with a love that could never be broken. But I forgot"

August 15, 2018 -Kim-

Chapter 1

June 2015:

It was June with the kind of heat when the weatherman doesn't have to tell you the temperature. He just says, "hot and sunny," which by the way, was shining extremely bright. The weatherman said that even after night fall, the temperature would not go down below 99°. The air conditioner was on full force, so it was cool in the house.

"It will use quite a bit of electricity while we sleep tonight."

"It's too hot to turn the air down." Tom mumbled.

We were sitting in the den watching golf, well, Tom was watching golf, I was mending his butt ugly, 187 year old favorite sweater passed down to him by his father, who received it prior to the league championship playoff game between the Chicago Bears and the Portsmouth Spartans in which Chicago won 9-0. It was his lucky shirt and he was right…it won the annual "ugly shirt contest" at the church every year since he received it.

I asked, "What time is it?" without allowing him time to answer, I continued, "they"…whoever "they" are, say that as you grow older, time seems to speed up and days run into each other."

He just grunted as he shifted his position in his recliner. He wasn't listening, as usual but it didn't bother me, I just continued talking. I guess after being married 29 years it doesn't matter if they hear you or not, they've probably heard it from you before.

"Sometimes I think that time is passing faster...then other times I'm not so sure." My first marriage felt very long, but it only lasted four years," I paused a moment. I had poked my finger with my needle, "...it felt like ten years."

I continued mending until with a smile I began to reminisce, "The kids were so precious back then, running all over the house. I wish you could have seen them back then." I glanced over to my sleepy husband wondering if he was just pretending to sleep or if he was listening.

"I would grab hold of one of them as they tried to run past me and say "Ha, Ha, I got you!" and they would giggle and squirm out of my arm to chase after their imaginary fairies."

I bit the thread away from the mended shirt. "Yeah, they were just as precious as can be...especially..." I recalled, "When we moved to mom and dads, God rest their souls... Did I ever tell you the story of when...?" I looked over at Tom who was now breathing heavy just as he does every afternoon when he snoozes in his recliner.

"Yes, I suspect I did."

"About forty-three times." he mumbled.

Must not have been asleep.

Reaching down to get my next mending job, I continued. "Well, when we moved out west, we had a cat that we put in the back of the truck and when we had to open the door, we wanted to be sure she didn't dart out and run away. So, the three of us lined up along the back end of the truck and held our arms up to catch her if she tried to make a break for it. Well, there we were, all serious, when I looked at the girls and they were so little that Linnie had to reach way above her head and little Anne couldn't even see into the trailer, but she had her hands stretched way up above her head ready to catch that cat should it try to jump out of the trailer." Laughing, I added, "She couldn't even touch the floor of the trailer!"

"Hmmm"

"It was so cute," I continued, "how they were going to stop their kitty from jumping out of the huge trailer." after a short pause, I considered just how fast they grew up. "Then after the girls got into school, I don't know what happened! I don't even remember their first days of kindergarten and now here they are all grown up with children of their own. I almost feel cheated!" I looked at Tom hoping for a sympathetic nod. "I feel cheated out of my time with my babies!"

He didn't answer.

Going back to my mending, "What time did you say it was?"

"I didn't." he snorted. "And shhh, I'm trying to watch the game."

"With your eyes closed, hum?" I said as I inspected a pair of jeans for holes over my half-moon glasses.

"Oh, yes..." I said to myself in a slightly quieted voice as I spotted the torn belt loop. "I remember now, it's Sunday...afternoon. We went to church this morning, got home at about 11:15, had lunch about an hour ago, so that would make it about...three o'clock. Yes...Sunday, June the 14th, three'ish." I was hushed again.

"June." I repeated to myself, the date was familiar. "June, 1970...8...yes, 1978"

June 1978:

A couple of days ago, I practically begged to go with him. I purposely waited until it was only a couple of days away before asking him one last time. I knew he would say no, he had already told me that I would have to stay in Chicago this time, but I just had to ask once more. I considered the possibility if he did say I could go, what would I do then?

"That's okay. It'll still work out."

It had already been a year. A little longer wouldn't make that much difference.

A girl from Bob's past had accused him of attempted murder. She claimed he threw her out of a second story window. Apparently, he had gotten mad and in the process of giving her a whipping, he became more enraged and threw her out of the apartment window. I really don't know much more than that, not that I didn't care, mind you, it's just that

I had learned not to ask questions about certain things, and this happen to be one of them.

It is amazing that she had even survived let alone that she filed charges against him. It's just not done in this business. Typically, the girl is so happy to get away, she accepts the "how" without looking back.

Bob denied the charges, of course, but... I knew he was capable of it.

Bob told me, as I had hoped, that I could not go to California with him, so I made him promise to call as soon as possible so I knew if he had won the case or not. I had told him numerous times throughout the last year how worried I was and how difficult it would be if he went to prison. Secretly, I relished in the idea, but no one even suspected I felt that way.

"I bet you'll win; I just want you to call so I know for sure!" I said in a whisper as I leaned up close to him.

He promised to call before he left the courthouse, which was exactly what I wanted him to say.

The day of Bob's departure, I told him I wished I could go. For effect, I bit my lower lip and looked to the floor. Bob put his arm around me and said, "I'll be back as soon as I can get a flight back here. I don't want to be in that state any longer than I have to." I timidly asked if at least, could I see him off at the airport. Interestingly, DeeDee did not appear to care whether she saw him off or not.

We said our good-byes at the gate, and we watched as he boarded the plane. DeeDee wanted to leave at that point but I insisted on waiting until the plane took off. She assumed it was because I was so sad to see him go. Truthfully, I wanted to be sure that he would not get off the plane without me knowing. "You can never be too careful." I said, "There have been times planes de-boarded because of a low tire or malfunction of sorts." I wasn't sure she bought it or not. However, it didn't matter. Whichever she chose to believe was just fine with me, Bob was on the airplane bound for a minimum of three hours away.

I never admitted it but honestly, I believed the girl who was suing Bob. I knew Bob was capable of much more than that. I've seen worse. You may not consider throwing a dog out of a window worse and I can't say it is either, but there was a time he had gotten very angry with Pepper, my sweet, gentle malamute. No one really paid enough attention to know when he needed to be taken out, so, he would have "accidents" now and then. Bob had no patience for animal crap or piss especially if he stepped in it. One day, while I was out of town, Pepper crapped in the house and Bob went ballistic screaming, yelling and more than likely, kicking and beating my poor dog, before throwing him out of a second-floor window. Pepper was a sweet, mild mannered ball of teddy bear fur. He couldn't help crapping on the floor, no one was taking him out and he couldn't hold it any longer. My sweet Pepper wouldn't hurt anyone unless he was protecting me.

I had taken Pepper out for a walk at our usual time. I was not in the habit of checking the courtyard for strays, but this one time as we began walking down the courtyard sidewalk, Pepper suddenly began to growl. There was another dog in the courtyard, and they locked eyes and it was on, the two went at each other's throats. Pepper had yanked his leash right out of my hand. I tried to call him off, but he wasn't listening. I was afraid if I tried to pull him away by his collar that I might be bit. Out of sheer fear of losing Pepper, I took a hold of his tale and pulled hard. The other dog, stood there looking very confused and Pepper turned his head toward me with a look that said, "Hey, what are you doing? I'm protecting you, here."

When I got back from visiting my family, I looked for Pepper. When I asked where he was, no one would say a thing, other than "he's gone". So, I went to ask my closest friend what had happened. She told me what happened and through tears, she said that Pepper had lain on the ground for a full day and a half before the animal league came and picked him up.

She said, "We didn't dare do anything, not with Bob's temper. So...we left him there." My eyes welled up as I listened to her story and thought of what Pepper must have gone through.

No more was ever mentioned about Pepper; however, I still grieve for that lovable creature, even now, forty-some years later.

The court date prior to the California hearing, was held at the Cook County Court house to determine if the woman could identify Bob, thereby determining if there was sufficient evidence to extradite him to California where the "alleged" act happened or dismiss the case entirely. I hoped for the first.

The day before the hearing, Bob surprised us all sporting a new look. When he came through the front door, we all clamored around to check out this new man of ours. He had gotten himself a curly perm and shaved his mustache and beard off.

"What made you get a perm?" someone asked in surprise.

"I just thought it would look good, is all." was his answer.

"Your mustache and beard?" asked another.

"Yeah, I thought I'd shave it off as long as I was changing my hair." Then with his arms outstretched he took a few steps back and grinned wide asking, "What do you girls think?"

No one dared say anything but "Great, you look sharp!" even though it would not surprise me if none of the girls genuinely liked this new look, I know I didn't.

He had told me once a while ago that he grew the mustache to hide a scar he had received in a knife fight. He was just vain enough that he didn't want people to see it, so he always had the mustache. He also had a thin line-beard that defined his jaw line and joined with the mustache at the corners of his mouth. In my opinion, it was one of his more striking features. His hair, which was typically combed back in a 1957 grease-ball look, was straight and fine. Another enticing feature that would eventually invoke fear.

This new particularly unflattering look of Bob's curiously came on the coming eve of his court date and not only did he change his appearance, but he was wearing a professional three-piece suit with a tie and he carried a briefcase, creating the image of another person entirely.

Bob was more adapted to wearing leisure suits than professional three-piece suits. I wondered why he was proposing this facade.

We sat in the back of the courtroom and he leaned over and told me his accuser was in the courtroom. "She's here, don't look, just pretend you don't know anything about her." Through the hearing, Bob wanted me to lean down so as not to be noticeable and he would do the same behind an open briefcase.

"I want it to look like I'm your lawyer." He whispered to me. "So, act like you're my client."

Of course, I did as he said. "But then", I thought to myself, "Why, may I ask, if you are so innocent, do you want to create such a ruse?" However, I kept my thoughts to myself.

A lawyer was asking the twenty-something year old woman a variety of questions, but it was when she was asked if she saw Bob in the courtroom that there was absolute silence. We ducked down and Bob began pointing to some papers in his briefcase.

"This is really unfair." I protested within myself, "You should sit up and let her try to identify you." I included a few choice words until I heard the girl answer her lawyer.

"No"

While I saw Bob exhale in relief, I said to myself

"I couldn't have identified him as far away as she was and with his new, never before seen, lawyer of the month costume, how could this woman, when she hadn't seen him in a few years pick him out!"

It looked as if Bob would get away with this barbaric act only because she couldn't identify him or even see him in the courtroom, however, when Bob visited with his lawyer after court, he was informed there was an order for extradition to California.

"Bob, you were spotted in the courtroom deliberately hiding from view. "

We had only been gone a few hours and as we walked through the door of the apartment, his mood quickly turned vicious. I tried to remember if I had said or done anything that might have made him mad until I realized he was not looking at me, his eyes were fixed on DeeDee. Everyone looked at Bob with fear in their eyes. Instinctively, they all took a step back. We had all learned that space was our best friend in these situations. I learned that a simple double arm's length could help to keep me somewhat clear of secondary rage.

I knew he wasn't after me, but I stepped out of range as a safety precaution. Bob's anger was directed at DeeDee, his legal wife whom he had married shortly after the act that brought him to this day.

"Do you see this?" he bellowed at her. "Do you, DO YOU??!!" His body became more rigid, his arms straight to his sides and fists ready for vengeance. His voice raised and distorting like the growl of evil, he pointed to his face, "This is the look of pure HATE! Pure, unadulterated hate for YOU!"

He continued shouting that she was an ugly, stupid, bitch. Then he spat on the floor and told her clearly that she was not worth the ground she stood on.

He slowly moved closer to her as she backed away. Her eyes were wide, and her mouth opened slightly as she looked for the right words to say. The words he would want to hear, the magic that would calm this evil. His rant continued as he approached her and with the back of his hand, he knocked her back against the wall where losing her balance, she fell to the floor. She quickly got back to her feet as Bob came within inches of her face screaming the only reason, he married her was so she couldn't testify against him. Even though DeeDee and I had never gotten along, I felt very embarrassed for her. He lit into her mostly with his words then stormed past her to the bedroom as he said he couldn't stand to look at her disgusting face, anymore.

DeeDee was trying not to cry but her tears betrayed her as she lowered her head to hide her embarrassment. I wondered which triggered her emotions whether it was why he married her or in response of being berated by the man she thought loved her. Whatever the reason, with tears streaming down her cheeks and mouth pinched tight, she desperately tried to regain her dignity. Suddenly, Bob bellowed for her.

"DEEDEE! GET IN HERE!"

At this, DeeDee jumped and ran into the bedroom. The beating would be worse if she had taken her time and we all knew it. Everyone quickly decided it was time to go to work and left. Nothing was ever said again about the incident after that.

Whoever said "a quick and speedy hearing" did not take into consideration the waiting time between court dates. Bob may have felt good about the time between court dates, but for me it seemed to take forever to arrive. I had always gone to court with Bob, but this time was to be different.

"This time I have to go alone," he said, "and hopefully, this will be it and we'll never have to worry about it again."

I smiled sorrowfully, "Okay, I'll be waiting to find out what happens." Bob appeared happy that I cared so much. Even his wife didn't appear to really care one way or another. It seemed as if it wasn't even real. She never talked about it or gave her thoughts as to whether or not he was guilty. But then, she couldn't express her true thoughts, if they were any less than being in his favor. Someone might say something.

Each time the phone rang that evening in June, I was right there as DeeDee answered. This day was "do or die" time. This day was my day. By 10:30 pm, I was beginning to wonder if we would get a call at all. I was very anxious for Bob's call. My mind ran away with me.

"What should I do if he's already on his way back?" The possibility of this happening could change everything! The past year would be nothing more but mindless desires of the worthless. A girl with a tainted past and even less of a future. "Who cares? She's a prostitute. She's nothing."

My fears were taking hold of me.

I shook my head, fiercely as I told myself I would not let myself go down. It would just take a little more time but would still work out. I was not going to allow myself to slip like that again. I was strong!

"What's the matter, Kim?" the voice came from behind me. I hadn't realized that anyone saw my reactions to my concerns.

"Nothing," I quickly answered, not wanting to share anything, "Why?"

"You look…" She searched for the correct word to describe what she saw. "You look…like you're worried."

I told her I was worried about Bob as well as, how things will turn out. She bought it.

"I'm sure he will be fine. If he was convicted, maybe he hasn't been able to call yet. And if he got off…we may not hear from him until tomorrow."

Just then, the phone rang. I just about knocked DeeDee down as I darted over to the phone.

"KIM!" DeeDee snapped as she reached for the telephone, "It's probably a trick!"

However, I didn't care, I had to know. As I stood there looking anxiously at DeeDee, she quietly indicated that it was Bob on the phone.

"Thank God!" I celebrated to myself, but I still needed to talk to him. I had to know the outcome and I wasn't going to leave that desk until I talked to him. DeeDee talked to him for an agonizingly long forty-five seconds before cupping the receiver and telling me that he won his case. It wasn't enough though, I had to hear it from Bob, myself. I raised my arms and smiled big so she wouldn't suspect anything. I wanted to be absolutely sure that all my planning would go off without a hitch and for that, I needed to talk to Bob personally.

"Bobby, she's jumping up and down now..." DeeDee said into the phone showing that I was going to bust wide open if I didn't get to talk to him.

It was official, Bobby was a free man. The court had found him not guilty of attempted murder and on the phone, he sounded happier than I had ever seen him. He actually sounded like a huge load had been lifted off his shoulders. I told him how wonderful it was and how "worried" I had been all day. In truth, I secretly hoped he would be found guilty, it would have made everything a lot easier, but he was found not guilty.

"Where are you?! Are you here yet? When will you be home?" I asked in rapid fire.

"Hold on, girl" Bobby laughed, "I'm at my motel tonight then I will catch the first flight back tomorrow morning."

I replied with enthusiasm, "Excellent! Oh, I'm so happy."

"The first flight tomorrow morning and I'm never coming back here again."

I handed DeeDee the phone back and walked towards my "never again" bedroom. Never again will I have an asshole in my room for ten minutes and thirty dollars. Never again, would I talk to a funky trick as if he was "the only one, for me". Never, never, never again!!

I wanted to wait until DeeDee hung up, but she was going on and on about the regulars that visited and how much money we had since he left, what he wanted to do when he got back, blah, blah, blah.

I casually went from the bedroom into the kitchen so I could check on her and see what the others were doing. They were sitting on the bed quietly talking. I turned around and casually walked back to my room.

"Still on the phone, CRAP girl! Get off the phone!" I yelled at DeeDee in my mind.

I couldn't wait. I had by now made three trips to the kitchen, anymore DeeDee might ask what I was doing while Bobby was still on the phone, but I just couldn't wait any longer! I couldn't stand it anymore! I couldn't wait for her to get off that DAMN phone for one more second! I got out a suitcase and began to pack as if I was getting ready to go on vacation.

It's all or nothing now. I was desperately trying to appear calm, yet my mind was reeling. When the others began to notice what I was doing, it felt as if I was being investigated by a group of old ladies standing at the gossiping fence taking turns looking over their shoulder at me.

"What's going on? Is Kim leaving? Does Bob know?" They whispered to each other

DeeDee, in the vain attempt to sound "just curious" rather than worried asked, "Kim? What are you doing?"

I looked towards her as I headed to the door with an armload of items, "Oh, I'm leaving."

Chapter 2

Not one person had a clue that I had been planning my "exit" for the last year, I saw to that. In fact, more than likely, they thought it was a spur of the moment act. If there was one thing I learned in my time as a ho, it was to trust no one so, for the entire year of setting up my exit, I never let on to anyone what I had been working for.

Other than a sixty-second conversation with Bob a year prior, I had never mentioned it.

I sat at the table in deep thought as I weighed out the pros and cons of telling Bob and if I was going to, exactly what words to use that would be the least threatening. It is really an unusual way to leave, telling your pimp that you want to leave is simply asking for a beating. It's a more common occurrence to run without thought and pray you aren't spotted by someone or found by your pimp.

In my fear, I considered the possible outcomes. I could see one of two reactions. I could see him trying to manipulate the situation with smiles and "But, why baby, I love you too much to let you go" or, and more likely, an angry look followed by "Girl, you ain't goin' nowhere." followed by a reinforcing beating. Nevertheless, I felt it was an important aspect to my plan.

"I have to do it now." I kept telling myself, "Now, now, it has to be done now."

I was so scared; I didn't know if I could go through with it.
"Maybe, I should just run." But it meant I wouldn't be able to get all of
my things.

"Remember, Kim," I told myself "Just tell him, and then agree to
whatever he says after that. Be that "yes ho" you've always been. It will
work, it will work." I repeated it over and over, "It will work, it will
work, it will work."

Just then, Bob walks in. "Hi Kim, what are you doing?"

My heart jumped up in my throat, I had not expected him to come in
until much later. "Do it, do it now!" I told myself.

"Uh, Bob, can I talk to you for a minute?" I asked trying to
maintain control and appear as calm as if I was asking if I could have a
buck for some smokes.

When I came back for another load, DeeDee handed me the phone
and said "Bob wants to talk to you."

"Crap!" I knew it would happen; I knew he would want to talk to
me. I tried to act as though I expected him to remember that we had
talked about me leaving a long time before this.

"Bob," I could feel my voice begin to tremble. I lowered my head
to regain my confidence "I..." then quickly looking up, prepared for
whatever would come next and with conviction said, "I want to leave."

I didn't give him but a split second to react before I continued "Not
right now." I assured him.

I watched his expression for any indication of how he would react,
knowing it could go either way.

"I wanted to tell you, while it was on my mind, but I HAVE to stay
at least until I know you are good with your court case. I have to know
that." I emphasized the necessity of waiting until after his court date,
whenever that would be.

Putting the phone up to my ear, I heard myself innocently say, "Hi,"
I wondered if I sounded like DeeDee and that phony sweet tone.

"Kimmy, what'cha doing?" he asked in that sickeningly sweet voice.

I repeated the same reply I did to DeeDee.

"Remember?" I asked as though we had talked only a couple of days before. "I'm leaving."

"But why? Why are you leaving now? We should be celebrating!" he continued with that same nauseating tone. He went on to tell me he loved me and that he thought I was going to pick him up at the airport.

"We can travel, now." he knew I loved seeing new places and cultures. "You can't leave now, just when we don't have this court case hanging over our heads anymore, not when we can really enjoy life." Bob was desperately trying to make it sound like he had some absolutely wonderful plans. He even sounded like I wasn't going to have to turn tricks anymore. In truth, he was taken so aback, he was grasping for the right maneuver to get me to stay.

Again, I asked if he had forgotten that we had talked about it and that he was okay with me leaving.

Bob looked as if I had put a gun in his gut. Quickly gaining his composure, he asked for confirmation "You will stay until my court case is over?"

"I told you I wanted to stay until your court case was over. You're okay, so now I am leaving." I was getting a sick feeling.

"Yes, but..." he began, then he quickly went from the all too familiar manipulating trap to the equally familiar vicious, threatening Bob, then back again, as he lost control then tried to regain control of the situation. He was too far away to be any real threat to me, which completely frustrated him. He pulled out all of his trickery to get me to wait "at least" until he got home so "he could say good-bye properly". I felt everyone's eyes on me. When I said "no", he would lose control again and go ballistic saying every thought that popped into his head from threats of what he would do when he found me to telling me I was worthless and he would never take me back. He played the "he was so generous and loving" card then telling me all I did was give him grief.

His attack went on so long and hard that I had to pull the receiver away from my ear so I would not have to listen to his so-called altruistic love and my unappreciative-childish behavior. He was good at intimidating and I felt it creeping up to me like a snake slithering up to its next meal. The reaction to purposely not listening to his rant was an utter shock to the others, including DeeDee who jerked her head back and opening her eyes and mouth wide, because she had never dared do that! No one had dared to be that bold as to not listen to him, even when she couldn't see him. It just wasn't done! He would know, he would know because he, well, he always knew.

"Kim must have a death wish" was surely crossing their minds at the time.

Oh, and what colorful language he used. For just a moment, it felt as if my eyes were welling up, but I took a deep breath and reminded myself to stay in control of my emotions. I had to reach deep down into the pit of my being and pull out every ounce of strength to maintain that control over the insults, accusations, and revengeful acts he was promising. It got so bad, that I forced myself to pull the phone away again, so all I could hear was faint angry words. I considered putting the phone down, but that would not be in line with the completion of my plan.

He finally told me he despised the very ground I walked on and would have nothing to do with me ever again.

Exasperated, he bellowed "Put DeeDee back on the phone! If I talk to you anymore, I will be physically ill." But he wasn't through, not by a long shot. He was not about to be out conned by a "worthless" whore.

Without a word or any expression, I handed the telephone back to DeeDee and calmly went back to my packing.

The others were now gathered together with concerned looks because no one tells Bob "no" and they heard it clearly from my lips, as well as, the hell and brimstone rant he laid on me.

After hanging up with Bob, DeeDee asked if I was still going to leave. I flatly replied "yeah."

But inside I was thinking, "ARE YOU NUTS?" I'm not a masochist, I'm not going to hang around to get beat up like Sue, or worse! WOW, He's pissed! Do you really think I'm that stupid?!"

My next trip to the car would be my last and it would be the scariest. Bob's reprisal would fall on the others if I was gone and they had to do whatever Bob had told them to do if they had any chance, but I couldn't think about that. I needed to stay focused on saving my own skin and as long as they don't jump me and tie me up, as long as I can get out to my car and lock the doors, I'll be okay...for the moment.

I had felt a warning earlier to keep my keys with me in my pocket and my purse was the first thing to go in my car. Every penny I had saved since Bob started letting us keep a stipend of our earnings was in that one piece of essential accessory. So, it was on that first trip I locked my purse in my car and put the keys safely in my pocket. Then, each trip after that, I locked the car before going for another load. This gave me a little security because I knew at that least one of the girls would think taking my purse or my keys leaving me with no money or means of transportation.

With a rapid pulse and nervous caution, I took a deep breath and went back for my last load.

Sammy, who I got along best in the group, asked if I would be willing to go out for a good-bye drink. I almost felt betrayed before I realized she was probably told to stall me.

"Anywhere you want to go!" Sammy promised.

With all of the girls around me, it was obvious they were trying to follow instructions to get me drunk so I would still be there when Bob got home. It was obvious because they weren't smart enough to do something outside of Bobs demands. It was also obvious they were not about to let me go without that drink. I felt a nudge and a whisper in my ear "Tell them okay, and then insist on a 2:00 bar." DeeDee tried to get me to go to a more popular place, which would have closed at 4:00 am, but that would give Bob enough time to get home. I held strong.

"You said anywhere and that's where I want to go." It was a little place not far from the apartment. And I insisted driving my car...alone.

"I may just leave from the bar. I'm not sure yet" I rationalized with them.

They had to agree, I didn't give them any other choice if they wanted me to go out with them. It was a case of who was going to grab the "brass ring" and I had my eye on that ring.

When we got to the bar, it was dark, quiet and empty. There was a long line of high stools pushed up to a long bar. On the other side lining a windowless wall were booths. We were the only people there at the time.

"Are you sure you want to go here?" DeeDee asked. "Don't you want to go somewhere we can dance?"

"No, not really, but if you all want to dance, they have a juke box." I mused.

No one seemed interested so, we took a booth at the very back and ordered our drinks. That familiar nudge and whisper, "order Crème-de-cocoa and cream". DeeDee paid, most likely on Bob's instructions and I wasn't about to. We sat and talked, and the drinks kept coming, especially for me. It seemed that everyone wanted to buy me just one more drink. They would not let me peacefully leave and I desperately wanted to avoid any physical altercation that might come out of the fear of any retaliation Bob might inflict.

"It's too early!" One would say.

"You can't leave yet, I just ordered you another drink." someone else said.

"You have to finish your drink; you've hardly touched it." another argued.

"You can't leave without just one more drink"

The excuses came one right after another until the bartender finally announced, "last call".

"Finally," I thought. "I've fulfilled my promise. Now I can get out of here, it's almost 2:00, it's closer than I would like, but I've still got time."

They wanted me to go to another bar, one that closed at 4:00 am. All of the girls were saying it was "too early to go home", now it was time for me to stand firm. I did not want them to see fear in my eyes, empathy does not exist in this world. Those that think her friends will be on their side will give you up in a quick second! Especially if it will put her in good with her pimp or stop her from getting a beating for whatever reason.

"You should wait until morning before you leave." They all insisted with a hint of concern.

"Naw, I think I am going to still leave tonight." I answered, knowing that their plans were to get me drunk enough that I would have to wait until morning when Bob would be back. It had already been three and a half hours since Bob's call and by my overly generous calculations, I would have another hour. That is if Bob had gotten on a flight as we were talking which was highly unlikely.

The girls kept pushing for me to stay "But, you've been drinking all evening, how can you drive?" DeeDee confidently reasoned.

With complete and utter satisfaction, I answered, "I'm okay, DeeDee. I've been drinking Crème-de-cocoa and cream."

"GOT IT! I GOT THE BRASS RING!"

She had forgotten about it, but now she knew what that meant, I had told her more than once that Crème-de-cocoa and cream has absolutely no effect on me. All the girls were drunk, I was not. This also gave me the upper hand.

"It doesn't make any sense, not really." I looked over to Tom, then the TV. Golf is still on, Tom is still sleeping. I always felt golf was boring and now I know it. "Anyway, it doesn't make sense. I have always been a cheap drunk, two beers and I'm gone… It wasn't until many years later that I began to wonder if God prevented this particular drink from affecting me because surely, He knew I would need to be straight that night… Well," I shrugged, "Whatever the reason, it worked, I saw it in DeeDee's eye's before she hung her head in obvious defeat."

All the girls tried to convince me to stay using one reason or another. "Get some sleep", "Start fresh in the morning." "You still have more to pack", "Let's go somewhere else for a few more drinks."

DeeDee accepted the defeat with one plea, no more conning, "If you leave," she quietly pleaded, "everyone will look at me as a fool. You and I have been here the longest and I'm staying."

"DeeDee." I answered, acknowledging her honesty. "I have to leave."

DeeDee knew I had to, as well.

"Check Mate"

Chapter 3

I noticed that Bob always seemed to know what was going on around him and what people were thinking, if you can imagine that. It seemed like he always knew when one of us was not where we were supposed to be as well as, our every thought even when he "appeared" to be asleep. It's a little hard to see, it was as if the man had an all-seeing eye in the middle of his forehead with a direct line to your thoughts 24 hours a day. It was as if he never slept because if you got up, he was asking what you were doing! He made a point of telling us that he knew everything about us, even more than we knew about ourselves.

It was his habit to drive around the city to look for us but pretend not to see us. Then later mention something about seeing you.

"Oh, Stephanie, I noticed one of your regulars was on State Street a little ahead of you." Other times he might stop one of the girls and ask, "Where's Judy?" then later he would comment that he saw her even if he didn't. It was easy to see how much he valued this ability and loved showing it off from time to time to keep us in line and afraid.

I was very depressed longing for freedom from my captor. As I walked the stro, I considered the idea of running and if I wanted to chance it because of my last attempt. Suddenly, Bobby happen to drive by. I wondered if he got a whiff of my intention.

"Wow that was close." I thought as I walked, "Five more minutes, I would have been busted heading for the bus station."

It was at that moment I realized I had gone out of my "designated stro" and I was heading south on LaSalle Street toward the Trailways bus station. I had not even convinced myself I was going.

In my depression I desperately wanted to leave, but I only had the clothes on my back and a little money that I had made that day. I was still weighing my choices when I saw the unmistakable long, shiny black Cadillac driving past me. He was on the other side of the street and appeared as if he hadn't seen me, I decided it would probably be "safer not to go". Later, at home, Bobby asked what I was doing that far away from the stro.

I fumbled with a feeble answer, however he knew, and he kept an eye on me for the next week or so.

I found "knowing" an interesting skill and thought it could come in handy every now and then. I began taking mental notes of how and what he did. I listened to things Bob would say to one of the girls and to what the girls would say to each other about Bob. I noticed that he was watching me taking these mental notes so adjusted my behavior accordingly and took note of him seeing me. I thought if I could "know" it would help me in many ways. It would help so I wouldn't get beat so much or get caught in other situations. I could manipulate a situation for my personally desired outcome.

I worked on it slowly, keeping all that I was learning to myself.

His ultimate goal at this "knowing" was to lead his stable into believing he had some sort of insight into our psyche as I said earlier but the truth of the matter was that he simply had a keen sense of observation with the ability to take that newly found knowledge and manipulate his prey through with irrational beliefs. I wanted to learn this skill but without his knowing.

We were all sitting at the dining room table, all were engaged in conversation, primarily about nothing. Josephine a tall, blond who wanted to get bigger boobs to pull more tricks along with Sherry who reveled in the idea of becoming the top ho, were on one side of the table. DeeDee was on the other side fairly close to Bob who was at the head of the table and I sat opposite to him.

Bob pulled out the thick wad of cash he always carried and began to count. No one paid much attention to this daily occurrence but continued to chitchat. It was a good time for me to practice a skill I had recently been working on with tricks.

Typically, Bob would have the higher denominations on top with the singles on the inside. This way, it would appear as if he had more than he actually did. The trick to my skill was having the ability to determine when the denomination changed.

When he finished counting the cash, he looked up at me and asked "Kim, how much do I have?" The odd question took me by surprise. I looked around the table and found the same surprised expression that I surely had.

I smiled and seemingly proud answered "three hundred and forty-eight".

Obviously impressed, Bob said "That's right." Smiling, he replaced the rubber band wrapping it twice around the bills then stuffed it back into his front pocket.

I was proud I knew the amount, but disappointed in myself that HE knew I was counting.

Chapter 4

The Chicago River that winds its way through the middle of downtown traditionally marks the boundaries between North and South Chicago. However, the true border, the border that is used by tricks, ho's and pimps alike, is not so defined.

If you head south past the river and past the ritzy hotels along Michigan Avenue you will begin to notice that the state of the buildings is beginning to lose that ritzy appearance. Continuing on you will come to notice the poverty you never knew was so widespread. The depressed homes and dilapidated hotels that were once so fancy that only the elite could afford to go beyond the foyer is now renting rooms out by the hour to anyone with a twenty-dollar bill and that don't ask if the sheets are clean.

"Oh, yeah, yeah, the sheets are clean." is what you will be told "The maid goes in at the top of the hour with freshly washed linen and a chocolate for each pillow."

Somewhere along that way, you will become more aware of the people and you'll wonder at what point in your drive did the white people leave and the blacks gather with looks of anger that seem to say how much they would love to put you six feet under. Finally, you will find yourself feeling like a frightened child in the dark forest full of hungry hyenas, so you lock your doors and turn around.

I can't tell you the exactly why, but for a white ho to cross into the black ho territory carries a death wish. I don't know the history and I can't tell you why it turned into black ho's only territory, all I know is I never considered going there. It's a matter of respecting the man and his ho's.

Bob had taken me too many "players" bars before, but this was the first time he took me alone to one on the south side. I felt surprised, a bit fearful, and extremely curious as to why we were there. The only purpose I could think of was to make a name for himself: "White pimp makes good in black man's world." a name he had battled for his entire career, a reputation he never truly reached and one that had haunted him until the day he died.

I could feel a little tension rising shortly after arriving, but I was with Bobby, so I wasn't too concerned. I sat at the bar facing the room while Bobby stood close with his elbow resting on the bar. He was talking to another pimp, I had no interest in their conversation, so I watched the people as they enjoyed the evening of no tricking. About half an hour in, I got up from my stool and motioned to Bobby I had to go to the bathroom. His eyes acknowledged my motions and he nodded his head ever so slight.

I made my way through the crowd to the bathroom and opened the door. There were only two stalls, and both were in need of a face-lift like the rest of the bar, but it was doable for my needs. I excused myself as I went past two ho's that were talking and went into the one open stall. When I came out a few moments later, I noticed the small room had an influx of ho's needing to use the toilet, however, as I got ready to go back and join Bob, I noticed an additional three ho's had quietly joined us in the small bathroom. That made a total of eleven ho's including myself in what might have at one time been a large closet. I squeezed my way through the ladies and up to the original two that were talking when I came in. They were now blocking the exit.

"Excuse me." I said to the ho that seemed to be the leader.

With angry eyes and crossed arms, she cocked her head and said, "Where do you think you're going?"

My first thought was "crap," but I said "I'm going out! Get out of my way, ho!" I was trying to go all "Pumba and Timon" on them but when I tried to push my way through, they didn't run, they attacked, all eleven girls with more trying to power through to join in pummeling the white ho. It must have been like watching the entire Denver Bronco's team tackling one opponent. Every center fielder, half back, and full back player jumping on top of the lowly opponent who was just wanting to use the toilet.

As I struggled against the barrage of kicks, punches, pushing, and insults, I let out a scream for help. "BOBBY..."

He came running with other pimps and began pushing, punching, and throwing girls off me as if they were a herd of rabid dogs. Then, just as quick, I felt the back of my shirt grabbed. I was lifted straight up and out from the center of all those mad dogs like a rag doll.

Before I knew it, I was being escorted out of the bar in a parade of black pimps and into the safety of Bobby's car. Bobby and the other pimps were punching and shoving girls away as we quickly made our way through the crowd of angry hos. It was surprising that these black pimps would go against their own ladies to escort this white pimp with his white ho out to a waiting car. But there I was, three in line ahead of me, one on either side and three or four trailing, and when we got outside Bobby said,

"RUN, don't look around, just RUN and get in the car!"

However, before I could get to the running car, I saw a black ho running toward us from across the street. She must have been told that a white ho was at the bar and was coming to join in the attack of the cracker stepping on their turf, the ho that dared to cross the understood boundary between black and white.

She was running full speed yelling "OUT'A MY WAY, NIGER, I'm GONNA GET THAT WHITE BITCH!" Not missing a beat, her man hauled off a back handed slap that stopped her in midair. Her legs flew up in front of her, knocking her flat on her back hitting her head on the hard concrete. He and Bobby then hustled me into the car and locked the doors so the defiant and rebellious hos couldn't get at me. They were still being punched, shoved and knocked to the pavement with a number of them still reaching us cussing, spitting and pounding the car with their vile outrage through the windows. Bob had reached the driver's side, jumped in and did not even hesitate as he hit the gas and raced through the crowd that was rapidly jumping out of the way. I knew, as well as they did, that Bob would run right into any ho that dared to stand in his way.

I wasn't sure which way to go from the apartment and I didn't have a map.

I knew the lake was behind me, so I pulled out and headed west. I felt a mix of fear, excitement and apprehension as I tried to decide the best route to take. I didn't want to go downtown to find the expressway, that would take too long. Bob could have phoned a friend of his who could be looking for me right now.

With every car I saw, my heart leapt up into my throat. "Do I know him? Is he one of Bob's friends?" Anyone of Bob's fellow pimps would not give a second thought to running me off the road to stop me.

As each vehicle went by me, I tried to see who was driving. I looked behind me, is someone following me?

The faster I get to the highway, the further away from him I would be, and the highway meant freedom, which meant life.

I was still on Addison when a vague memory invaded my anxious thoughts of a highway, no, expressway just beyond a high school Bob let me go to complete my high school education.

"Lane...Tech, yes, it's just a couple of blocks past Lane Tech." But as I approached the high school, I could not see any crossing highway.

"Where is it!?" I began to panic, "It's there," I told myself, "It's there."

Passing the school building, I continued to panic.

"It's there, I'm sure of it." I assured myself but it wasn't coming fast enough.

It felt as if each second was an hour. With an increasing and pounding heartbeat, I kept fearful lookout behind me. I knew Bob couldn't possibly be back yet, there has not been enough time.

I went over it in my head for the third time.

Bob called at 10:30 pm. He said he was at the hotel.

He was supposed to catch a flight the next day but with the present situation, he may catch the next flight out, how fast could that be?

I'm sure he had full faith in my dedication and no fear of anyone leaving this late in the game. They would naturally leave as soon as Bob got on the airplane to go to court. No one had, he had no worries.

IF he was at the airport when he called and already had his ticket in hand, which was not likely because he had complete faith I would be there, and got on the airplane immediately, which is also unlikely, he could arrive four hours later at 2:30 am. He would then have to get a taxi home or have someone at the airport waiting to drive home, putting him back at 4:00 am.

Conclusion: the absolute earliest he could be at the airport is 2:30 am. It was 2:15 am. I had illogically fifteen minutes to one hour and forty-five minutes.

My heart was pounding, and my breath was heavy and labored as the Kennedy Expressway loomed into view. There was a small sense of relief with the highway, my lifeline, was just twenty seconds ahead, however, those twenty seconds, now seventeen seconds, were countered by the awareness of each yard, no, each foot on the street's pavement. The closer I got to the on-ramp of my long-anticipated freedom, the longer each measured foot took.

"It's right there...is he somewhere, somehow behind me?" A quick look in the rearview mirror told me I was now the only person on Addison Street. "Almost there."

My thoughts were frantic but focused, "Finally, the on-ramp, up there, two no five more seconds, five hundred feet. I've almost made it, I ... made it. I'm here! I made it!"

"Turn," I told myself, "it's right there, turn now, turn, TURN!"

I had never made him angrier than I had that night. Since I had been with him, his anger could have been viewed as nothing more than a childish temper tantrum. This time, however, I have humiliated him. Oh, I had made him angry many times and saw the backhand of that rage more times than I care to acknowledge or remember. But this time I made a fool out of him. This was not my intention, but it sure ended up that way.

Outside of Chicago about halfway through Illinois, I stopped at a little place and called. DeeDee made me promise to call the apartment every hour. I really didn't want to talk to her or Bob when he got back, but it would help me to keep up with his where a bouts. DeeDee said I could call collect, so I did. She accepted the call and immediately said, "Hi, where are you?"

"I really don't know, some little rest area." I lied. "Is Bob home, yet?"

"No, Sheri just went to get him" She replied.

3:30 am: He must have taken the next flight he could get on. Probably while we were at the bar.

I was anxious to keep going so I told her I was fine, and not a bit tired.

"Okay" She said, "Well, give me a call in about an hour, Bobby should be home then, and he said he was really worried about you driving while being up so long."

"Okay, but I'm wide awake, *(no doubt the adrenalin racing through me)* talk to you then." I answered and quickly hung up.

I was glad that call was over. I felt confident that DeeDee was telling the truth about him not being back yet, however, there was also the chance that he had gotten home and had taken off to find me, right away.

"No time to overly relax, not yet."

Back in my car, I felt a little more at ease. I knew I was going to have to call again if this was going to work.

Tom broke my concentration, looked at me and asked, "Why call? Why not just forget it and keep going?"

It was a way for me to keep an eye on Bob. To see when he got back from California and when he had taken off to look for me. Once I knew he was on the way, I could go from the fastest and most logical route to a longer, slower more illogical one. I also wanted them to think I was really stupid and that...was logical.

It was a case of 'knowing', manipulation, and control.

Chapter 5

Kiki had run off. Bob knew she was headed to her home in Indiana.

Matter-of-factly, Bob announced, "I'm not going to get her. She's not worth the hassle."

Kiki had not been with us but for a short time, anyway, she really was a bad pick. Bob once said that oriental girls don't usually work out. They tend to run off as soon as they can.

"Each time a girl has run, I have known where she has gone." He looked around the table. "They always go home! I can go get them anytime I want." He paused to light a cigarette. We quietly watch as he took a deep drag. A small cloud of smoke trying to escape was quickly drawn back in. He trapped it in his lungs as if he was smoking a joint then spewed it out in a straight line that reminds me of the steam released from a train whistle as it approaches a crossing or maybe a paddlewheel boat saying hello to the river homes along its travels. I wondered if he had more to say, or if his cigarette signified the end of his steamboat strutting, but we listened for his next words anyway.

Bob did not disappoint us, "The smartest way to hide is to hide in plain view."

"You didn't move out of there?!" I was shocked she still had the Armitage Avenue apartment. Why in the world would you chance that?"

"Everyone thought I moved out, but..." She explained. "I decided I wanted to keep paying the rent, it gave me a quiet place to go when I needed time by myself."

"How'd you get the money to do it?" I asked in shock.

"I held out some of what I made and paid the balance with tricking on the side." She explained.

It sounded a little iffy and it made me nervous to think about living in one of the old apartments, but she assured me it was very safe.

"I've had it for the last three months," She assured me how she was positive Bob would not think of finding us in there. "Like I said, it's been three months."

When Sammy ran, Bob asked me if I knew why she left and where she was going. It scared me and I got worried that Bob might suspect we were going to run together.

"Well, Kim!" he was getting a little upset, "Do you know where she went? You two were pretty tight, she must have told you something!"

"No, she never told me," was all I could manage.

My "knowing" was not working right then, he had caught me off guard. In fact, it made him so angry that I wasn't saying anything, and he got a little more forceful with his questioning.

"BITCH! If you know something, you better tell me!" His eyes began to squint and the furrows on the sides of his nose began to rear up. When his mouth got that thin straight line, I leaned back away from him and in a panic, I spewed "I DON'T KNOW."

That night I ran.

It had been our plan to run at separate times to throw him off. So, when I showed up at her door, she was surprised to see me. She hadn't expected me for another week.

Two days had gone by without any problem, so we finally began to enjoy our freedom. However, it would be short-lived.

We were so cocky confident that we stepped out as if we hadn't a care in the world. That is until our eyes met with Bob's as he was *coming up the walk. He picked up the speed after us as we turned and ran back inside the apartment building.*

We ran up the steps to the second-floor apartment and in a panic ran toward the back of the building where there were wooden steps leading down to a parking lot. Upon opening the door, we were then met by DeeDee, who was halfway up the steps. Her expression told me that she was just as surprised to see us coming out as we were seeing her coming up. I turned and pushed Sammy into the doorway where we ran up the steps to the third floor and began frantically pounding on the first door we came to. I would have broken the door down if I thought I could get away from Bob, but the door was incredibly old and made of heavy, solid wood. It was meant to last forever.

The middle-aged occupants took what felt like a long time, but we weren't about to stop pounding. When they finally made themselves known, they asked through the closed door what we wanted. Obviously, they were worried about who these frantic girls were pounding on their door.

Together we shouted, "WE'RE BEING CHASED, LET US IN, LET US IN!"

They told us to call the police and leave them alone. "PLEASE! LET US IN. PLEASE" we frantically pleaded with them.

The Man hesitantly opened the door only enough to get a better look at the unwelcomed visitors. We weren't about to gracefully introduce ourselves, we pushed our way through and past the man and in a frenzy, we attempted to explain that there was a man after us and that we were afraid he was going to kill us. A woman came from the kitchen area and said she called the police and they would be here in a few minutes.

DeeDee and I continued to talk over each other as we tried to explain that we needed to hide and pleaded with them not to open the door to Bob. Suddenly, BAM, BAM, BAM "Police!" came from outside of the door.

We begged the man not to open the door. We feared it was Bob pretending to be a cop to get into the apartment.

"Nonsense, we called the police, it has to be them." he balked as he calmly answered the door. The police entered the apartment to see Sammy and I huddled together shaking uncontrollably. The man was talking to the police when Bob stepped into view. I felt my knees begin to buckle and my heart felt as if it exploded within my chest and sheer terror filled my entire being.

Bob looked at us, then very polite and respectfully, smiled at the cops and asked to speak to them in the hall. We knew what he was telling them. We just knew he was explaining that we were simply two runaway whores of his and he was just there to reclaim his property. After a few moments, Bob extended his hand and shook hands with both cops. I stared in disbelief and turned to Sammy who was in shock, as well. They didn't even look back at us, they simply left!

To Serve and Protect went out the window with a three-minute conversation and a handshake.

Iowa City, I could see the lights of the city from a distance. It feels like I've gone a lot further than Iowa City. Still, I felt like I had reached another steppingstone crossing a river. I learned that Bob had gotten back to the apartment. I knew this because the last time I called, he got on the phone talking just as sweet as you could imagine.

"Hi baby, are you okay?" he was laying it on thick and sickeningly sweet as if it was dripping in honey.

"Yea, I'm fine. Did you just get back?"

"Yep, just walked in the door. Where are you?" he replied.

I told him I did not know, which of course, was a bald-faced lie, but I didn't want him to know how far I had gotten.

He asked if I was still on interstate 80. It was the most logical route to take. I answered him with a "Well, yeah, I guess I didn't know there was another way", with a quick little roller coaster tone in my voice to sound like I was dumber than a rock.

"You have been up for so long, darling, why don't you stop for a while and get some rest." attempting to lure me into a spot he could easily find me. "Maybe if it's not… too awfully far, I could come and see you one last time. We could…" blah, blah, blah. blah-blah whatever, whatever blah-blah.

I told him that maybe he was right.

"There isn't any motel close by here, but maybe I'll go down the road and find a place."

"Will you call me and let me know where you're at?" he sweetly asked. "I would like to give you a proper good-bye."

Bob had DeeDee take Sammy back to Addison Street and I was to go with him. I wasn't sure what this meant. Why does he want to separate us? Why does he want me to ride with him? Back at the apartment, as I expected, that evil reared his ugly face and came at me full force. Sammy had run off from DeeDee when they reached the apartment, so I was left to receive the full brunt of Bob's wrath.

When we entered the apartment, I made the mistake of keeping my back to him, which granted me an unexpected kick in the rear end. The beating came in a barrage of insults, back handed blows, and being spat in the face. Around the room stood four frightened girls each one of them against the wall. They knew it was going to be a bad one and we all knew if I tried in any way to retaliate, the beating would be worse so they wanted to stay as far from misplaced blows as possible. A good defense, as long as you weren't the intended target.

As I stood looking at him waiting for the next blow, Bob said "DeeDee, you've wanted to punch her out since she came to us, well

here's your free shot. No repercussions and I won't let her hit you."
DeeDee glanced over to me standing there showing next to no emotion.
"Well, girl?" he repeated, "Here's your chance."

DeeDee hesitantly walked over and stood in front of me and looked
into my eyes. I saw something I had never seen in her before. For a
moment, I felt a connection and look of empathy. Empathy, something
until that very moment I would not have believed was in her. However, I
was not about to allow this girl to take her frustration out on me without
consequences. I return the look with a look that said, "I will get my
revenge". I looked her in the eyes un-moving as I prepared for a blow
to the gut or face. She would pay for her actions... at a later date.

"No," the word came from her lips. "I don't think I will."

I'm not sure, if it was pity or if she understood what I was saying to
her through my eyes. I would prefer to think she understood what I was
going through and she chose not to add to the trauma. Whatever the
reason, she turned toward Bob and reaffirmed her choice to not exact
her long-lived contempt on me. Equally surprising, Bob did not insist
she take a swing at me, instead he continued his own assault. As he
came towards me, panic caught a hold of me once more. I saw those
eyes, the ones that turned black with evil as he approached. I had
nowhere I could run.

I checked his arms, "Are they rigid? Do they go down his side,
unmoving? Are the hands clasped into molded balls of white steel or
were they relaxed?"

Knowing what he had done in the past to countless others I tried to
prepare for the inevitable blow that, as he has said many times, "would
leave no marks".

I slowly backed up, but not too far. The windows were behind me.
Those same windows that saw my tender dog, Pepper, thrown out with
those same cruel arms. The same unrelenting cruelty that takes hold
without regard or thought of anyone other than satisfying its lust for
control and inflicting sadistic pain then to follow it with sex.

There they are, those rigid arms, the readied fists, together with the
eyes that bored a hole through the skull. His steps came toward me with

a controlled intensity. I couldn't help it, "You're crazy!" I screamed, "You're crazy!"

"Oh, I'm not crazy..." that evil black in his eyes shown through as he narrowed his focus on me. "And I have a paper to prove it!"

I held my hands up to defend myself, though I knew it was futile to try. I then stepped behind a chair. Maybe in an attempt to thwart a heavier blow. It didn't work, Bob took hold of it and threw it to the side as he lunged for me. He grabbed hold of me and tossed me as if I was a second chair. I fell to the floor, but quickly gained my footing. I was not about to put myself into that much of a vulnerable position making it easier for him to exact his revenge on me for wanting out. I knew what he wanted to see was tears and usually I could muster up a few, but this time was different. This time tears would not help.

He threw me again, this time he hit me with such force it knocked me to the floor where he would grab me by the lapel of my shirt and throw me again.

His final act of revenge for what I had done was to force the barrel of his pistol into my mouth, as he fiercely swore, he was going to blow my head off. Interestingly, I wasn't worried about being killed. I'm not even sure I thought he would do it. What kept running in my head was not what you might think but how he would want me to hold this gun barrel in my mouth. A queer thought with an enraged mad man holding a pistol in your mouth, but my concern was that I did not want to make him any angrier than he already was.

Bob became quiet for a moment as I fidgeted with an effective way to hold the foul metallic tasting pistol barrel in my mouth then that anger was quickly replaced with hysterical laughter. No one was curious enough to come find out what was so funny, they had all seen what he had done and the evil that seemed to overtake him. Through his laughter he hollered out, "She looks like she's sucking a dick." He removed the gun from my mouth, but the laughing continued, which ultimately ended the rampage.

Thirty minutes later, I was coming to the last of the Iowa City exits. "I think I'll call again." I said aloud, even though no one else was in the car. I went on to clarify to myself exactly why I was going to call and why after only thirty minutes.

"I want to know if he is still there waiting on a call from me to mindlessly tell him he can come and beat my brains out now or if he has decided he didn't want to wait and has taken off to find me with the same loaded pistol."

This would be my last call.

When DeeDee answered the phone, I asked to talk to Bob.

"Oh, He was so tired from his trip he decided to go to lay down for a little while, but he should be up soon."

My first thought was Uh huh, "Do I have STUPID written on my forehead!!??"

DeeDee hadn't realized that she had just told me that Bob was on his way and it was time to throw it into high gear, add a bit of confusion and disappear like a wisp of smoke caught by a rogue breeze.

Back in my car, my heart started pounding, my breath abandoning me. I felt each beat within my sternum and pushing against each lung to the side creating a quick spastic jolt as the air was momentarily halted from entering my starved lungs. I kept my eye on the rear-view mirrors as well as looking for a highway going to the south. "Maybe I should go north." I questioned myself. In my head, I knew he could not have traveled clear across Illinois and into Iowa within the thirty minutes between the time I talked to him and my last call, but fear was attacking me from all directions. I had to get off interstate 80, that… I knew for sure.

Chapter 6

Bobby had warned me there might be someone in the bar that had a beef with him. So, walking in, I wondered why Bob wanted to go in. We could have very easily avoided any possible riff by just going to another players bar. But as the saying goes, "Mine is not to wonder why, mine is but to do or...die."

Bobby led me over to a table and we sat down. His eyes scanned the bar as the waitress took our drink orders. When she left to get our drinks, Bob leaned toward me, discretely handed me a pistol and said.

"He's here, don't look around, just act normal and if something happens, I want you to go outside and get the car ready to go, understand?"

I nervously answered, "Yes" as I put the weapon in my purse under the table.

We had just about finished our drinks when Bob saw the other man making his way over to our table.

"Ready?" Bob asked as he stood to confront his vengeful opponent.

I stood and took a step out of the way. Others began gathering and without so much as a word spoken, Bob's antagonist leapt forward shoving Bob into the same table I was sitting at only a moment ago. I didn't wait to see what happened next, I turned toward the door and took off running, pushing the onlookers aside.

I ran to the car started it up and moved to easily take off. As I waited there in the driver's seat for Bobby to come out of the bar, a chain of cars surrounded me. It appeared to be a traffic jam, so I attempted to get them out of the way. I beeped the horn and continued to even though they didn't appear to make any attempt to move.

"MOVE!" I yelled as I laid on the horn in a futile attempt to free Bobby's car. But my efforts to be freed would be met with an immovable fortress.

When the police came, sirens screeching the announcement of their arrival, I am reminded of the 1975 Andy Kaufman's performance of The Mighty Mouse theme song announcing, "Here I come to save the day!" I had already learned that the police were no help in times of need, at least for people like me. However, this time they were a somewhat welcomed sight because the traffic suddenly gave way as everyone screeched off to avoid any confrontation with the cops and I was left with the realization that I had been made a fool. Those in that chain of Cadillac's, LTD's, and Lincoln's that had made up a sort of barricade had been ordered to stop me from getting out while Bobby was to be murdered inside the bar. More than likely, I would have been kidnapped and forced to work for someone else or murder number two.

I feared what was to come next. Should I leave or stay? Is Bob lying on the floor in the bar soaked in his own blood? Am I going to jail? Question whorled around my mind like race cars in racing around a track going nowhere fast. I just didn't know what to do. I turned to look toward the bar door when I was met with the sudden sight of Bob as he was slammed against the car door and knocked to the ground.

I took in a small breath of shock at this sight and then I looked to see who shoved him, I saw the culprits were three cops. Two immediately dove for Bob pulling him up by the lapel and once more slamming him up against the car door by the weight of one cop and held there by his forearm against Bobby's throat.

A sight I never would have expected to see, Bob getting knocked around without retaliating.

I wondered if the car door had been dented.

Once again, it felt an eternity as I drove toward the exit. I thought I would begin to feel better once I was on a southern route, but I think I was even more panicky than ever now that I knew Bob was headed out after me. I had to calm myself so I could think. So far, my thinking was completely logical. Learn when Bob arrives in Chicago while everyone there tries to keep track of where I was. Logical. Take the obvious route as long as I could to get to Colorado as fast as I could. Logical. Now, I had to think "illogically". If it was logical to go straight west on I80 it would be illogical to take a small state highway south. Illogical. I then look for a small highway going south and found one going south…east. Seriously illogical. It was a crazy way to get to the western states, but… it wasn't what he would expect from a stupid bitch.

Chapter 7

June 6, 1974

School was out for summer. The 1972 single by Alice Cooper, SCHOOLS OUT was blasting through the intercom in every room and hall of the school. Everyone was running out of the school, shouting and throwing their books, paper, pencils and any other supplies they had all over the school yard. It had been the same every year and Alice Cooper's hit had become the tradition since in first blasted free on the radio stations.

Leaving school on the last day was certainly a sight and would continue even though the principal threatened us all if we threw all of our supplies all over the yard that our grade cards would be held, parents would be called and we would return to clean up the mess, but it never happened.

Summer was exciting, but this year was going to be even more of an exciting time for my friend Carmen, my brother, Matt and Bear, my brother's friend. For the last couple of months, we had been planning this big adventure that would take place once school was out. Carmen had completed her high school requirements to graduate, but I was short half of one credit. However, at seventeen I didn't care, I was more interested in the big journey. We were going to move out and conquer the world, just the four of us, well, at least move to Chicago!

Boarding the bus in Cleveland was exciting. I had never ridden in such a huge vehicle. I could actually stand up and not hit the roof! They even had a bathroom in the back! We found our seats and got comfortable anxiously ready to take off!

The ride became very boring very quick but arriving in Chicago renewed that same exhilaration we felt at the beginning of our ride. We were so excited we could hardly stay in our seats until the bus pulled into the station and the driver said we could "depart and go into the depot."

The city had a different feeling and the smell was different as well, but we didn't care, we were in Chicago. Home of Al Capone, and Bugs Moran, and there were more people and vehicles than we could count. "WOW!" I said as we were busting at the seams with eagerness to see the attractions of the city coupled with the energy we were picking up from all those people bustling around.

As we gazed on what our first glimpse of city life would be, Matt asked the obvious question that none of us even thought about up to then.

"Okay, which way should we go?"

The four of us looked at each other as if to say, "Oh yeah, which way should we go?"

We were all standing around with our thoughts reeling when Matt suggested "How about that way?" He was pointing to the north and it was as good as any, not knowing the city, so we agreed and began our search for a restaurant and hotel we could stay in.

The walk was long, and we were getting hot and tired. The guys were carrying our luggage, which was definitely a help for me and Carmen, but they were even getting tired and the suitcases were feeling much heavier than they were.

After what felt like an eternity, we finally spotted a hotel a couple of blocks away. It wasn't much but it was a place to sit and rest and at that point, we just didn't care as long as we could sit and cool off.

"What do you think?" Matt asked.

We were drenched in sweat and wining like little lost puppies, "Let's do it"

Reaching the hotel, we noticed many strange looks as we walked into the old building. But we quickly forgot that when we felt the cool air in the lobby. It was wonderful and we felt our spirits rising for the third time, which, of course, made us forget how miserable we were feeling just ten seconds ago.

A rather large man dressed in what looked like a very old and worn English golfers outfit stood by the registration desk talking to a shorter fellow. They didn't seem to take note of us until Matt interrupted their quiet conversation.

"Excuse me, sir, but could you tell me how much two rooms would cost?" He asked them with the mustered confidence of a world traveler but feeling as intimated as a strawberry patch in the midst of a field of collard greens. The pudgy sort'ta golfer man and his rather disjointed desk clerk looked puzzling at each other as if they did not understand the question.

My thoughts ran to "What's the big problem? They are running a hotel, why would they have a problem with this question?"

Both men looked at Matt then looked at the rest of us. "Uh, for two rooms?" The clerk asked. "For how long?"

"Uh, well, I don't know," Matt answered as he turned to see what the rest of us thought.

We shrugged; we just didn't know what to say.

"A couple of weeks? How about two weeks," Matt then asked us "Do you think that should be good?" Addressing the clerk, he went on, "Umm, yes sir. What would it cost for two rooms for two weeks?"

Again, the two men just stared at the four of us.

"I don't know," The bellman finally said "Go ask Frank. See what he says."

"WOW" tried very hard to come out of my mouth, but I bit my lips so the rude "wow" would not escape.

The clerk must have thought that was a good idea and as he went, the sort'ta golfer man, who turned out to be a bellman, made small talk with us.

"So…are you from here?" He nervously asked. We chitchatted for a while until the extremely confused clerk came back and told us it would cost $140.00...plus tax.

Matt counted out the money and the bellman grabbed the keys and offered to carry our luggage up to our rooms. It surprised me that he would do that, and I felt like royalty. Then Matt took a hold of the bags and said, "I have them." with a smile.

As we walked to the elevator, I noticed that it looked like something straight out of the Great Depression era. The bellman opened the heavy door that seemed to take all of his strength, to reveal a collapsing gate. He then opened the gate and we all filed into the small room. The bellman closed the gate and the heavy door slowly closed. I'm guessing, the door might have had a mechanism on it that kept it from slamming into your ass before you had a chance to get into the elevator.

I looked around the little elevator room for the floor button, but this elevator had a hand-operating lever to go up and down! (yep, depression era, Al Capone, Bugsy Moran) sort'ta golfer -man took hold of the lever and pulled it back towards him and the rickety old box creaked and moaned as it slowly moved up the levels. I didn't know whether to be in aw or to be fearful of what surely is the equally ancient cable carrying us up. We could see each floor as we passed the gated doors with the floor number hand painted in large numbers. Three…Four…Five. He began slowing down as we passed the fifth floor by moving that lever forward until we reached the sixth floor. Again, I felt another WOW trying to escape my lips when I saw he was actually able to bring us to a perfectly level stop.

He led the way down to the end of the hall to which another hallway crossed. One room would be to the right and the other to the left. The bellman in the scruffy golfer-outfit turned to Matt and Bear as he struggled for the right words.

"Uh…" the bellman fumbled as he tried not to assume anything or insult us, "Who goes into which room. Boy, girl, boys, girl, girl?" He really struggled with this question until Matt finally realized what was going on and politely told him that Carmen and I would be in one room while he and Bear would take the other. It was obvious the relief the bellman felt.

"Whew, I'm glad that's over."

We had a laugh at the clerk and bellman's expense but wondered why the strange exchange, why didn't they know how much a room was? Why were these hotel employees so confused about renting hotel rooms?

In close to a week we had no luck finding a job. The guys wanted desperately to be the breadwinners so Carmen and I would not have to worry about that. We had tried to spend as little as possible, never going out to eat and buying only cheap non-perishable foods from the store. Still, money was rapidly dwindling and soon we were eating and drinking powdered breakfast drink, we were bored, hot, hungry and frustrated.

We were also running low on smokes. Matt and Bear always seemed to come up with a pack or two of Winston, Marlboro or a cheaper generic brand, so Carmen and I began to go the boy's room to mooch one to share. I wondered if they had a carton, they were holding out which they denied. They also denied stealing them, but truthfully, we didn't really care just so long as they forked one over now and then. Nicotine fits are difficult at any age.

On a particularly boring evening, I was sitting on the bed while Carmen was looking out of the window.

"Hey," she called to me. "Come check this out."

She had spotted some men hanging out on the street down below our window. There was a rainbow of pastel colored polyester suits with... matching wide brimmed hats. Carmen was a little more streetwise then I was at the time and said they were probably pimps.

"Really?" I asked in shock.

"Yeah, I bet they are."

"Hey, I got' a idea." I snickered. "Let's put a little orange drink powder in one of those paper cups and see if we can pop one of them on the head!" We about knocked each other over as we both turned to get the first paper cup to drop. Carmen awarded me the honors.

Our first drop missed its target but drew curious looks. I do not know why, but they decided not to watch awfully long to see if we would expose ourselves.

POW! Direct hit! Orange all over that lime green hat. We fell to the floor hiding just under the window laughing at the bulls' eye Carmen made but peeked up too soon and was spotted.

"Girl, what you doin' up there?" hollered our victim, surprisingly not upset. Carmen decided to answer back.

"Bein' bored!" she yelled down to the colorful thin men.

"Well, come on down!" he returned.

"No, I don't think so." Carmen answered.

They continued to try to get us downstairs or to give them our room number so they could come up until we simply stepped away from the window.

When we told the guys about the fancifully dressed men, they seemed curious about them, but warned us not to repeat the Tang-bombing.

"You don't know who they are or what might happen or what they would want." Matt warned. We promised to relieve our boredom in other ways that were not so dangerous.

A couple of horribly boring days later we happen to notice that there were a large number of visitors our adjacent neighbor welcomed. I wondered if it was drugs sales, but Carmen figured that she was probably a prostitute and the visitors were her "customers".

"WOW!" I said. I was in absolute shock that a real prostitute was actually... right... next... DOOR! It did make sense though, flashy men outside waiting on their "ladies" to finish up for the night so they could get their money. They usually showed up in the early hours of the morning and left until the next early morning.

We tried the glass against the wall trick when we would hear a new "customer" knock on her door, but all we heard was muffled words we couldn't identify.

"Hey, I got an idea!" Carmen whispered with a devious smile, "Wanna have some fun?"

After she explained her idea, I was a little hesitant and did not know if I could pull it off, but the boredom was taking hold and the demand for anything to break that tiring feeling was throwing our commonsense right out the window on top of those orange, green and pink hats.

"We'll wait until someone knocks on her door and then we'll open our door, apologize and say something like "These walls are so thin, it sounded like you knocked on our door." Then we'll shut the door before the hooker answers her door" She giggled. It sounded like fun, but I was still unsure if I could pull it off. Carmen said she would do the talking this time and I can the next time if I wanted.

We didn't have to wait long before we heard another knock on her door. Giggling, we hurried so we could play out our ruse before the girl opened her door. Again, we almost fell over each other as we tried to reach the door first.

"One...two...three" and we opened the door. What we found was a stocky older man standing in the hall. At first with a shocked look in his eyes, then a smile.

"Oh, my goodness," Carmen innocently told the stranger.

The man turned toward us and began asking if he could go with us instead of "her". I didn't know what to say, I was too embarrassed, but Carmen just as calmly as you could imagine smiled and said "Oh, no, we better not, she's expecting you..." She didn't have time to say anything else because all of a sudden the prostitutes door flew open and a rather disheveled young lady took one look at us and then without a word, grabbed a hold of the man by his brown polyester jacket and pulled him inside. We were pleased with our little stunt.

Shortly thereafter, there were some frantic muffled voices, a door loudly being swung open before slamming shut, followed by the unmistakable sound of someone running down the hall. About five minutes later as we were talking about what might have happened, there were several different voices quickly entering the prostitutes room.

We heard someone say in a hushed voice, "How did this happen? Is she...?"

Carmen and I looked at each other.

There were some more hushed voices and I thought someone asked if they should call the police. A very insistent man answered, "No, we can't do that!"

"What should we do?" a voice asked.

"I don't know, but we have to get rid of her. We can't leave her here." another answered.

Then we heard someone ask about calling a certain person but we couldn't understand who the voice suggested calling. We tried the glass against the wall trick again to no avail.

We learned later that prostitutes do not count among the human race. Other than Matt and Bear, we would never mention the nameless girl whose body was treated with no dignity, no respect, she was just disposed of quietly.

Carmen and I decided with the rapidly moving week and no money to stay even one more night, it was important that we joined the guys in finding jobs. We had decided it was up to all four of us if we were to make Chicago a go. We had no money, so there was no other option.

The street was busy with all types of people. I had never seen so many in a two-block area. The bars and stores all appeared to be busy so maybe it's a good area for Carmen or me to find a job. Our skills were not very wide, I had worked at McDonalds, a pizzeria, and volunteered at the hospital coffee shop as a candy striper, Carmen had never had a job. Legally our prospects were even less. We were only seventeen, which meant, we were too young to work at the restaurants because they served liquor.

However, we weren't beat yet, we were going to make it. Our biggest encouragement to forge ahead came from, none other than teenage stubbornness...and our bellies.

The next day we went out to pound the pavement looking for a job. We were crossing the street and discussing the dire situation we found ourselves in and where we wanted to go from here. The guys were a bit upset with our decision to join the hunt, but we felt four bodies looking was twice as good as two.

Matt and Bear were not chauvinistic, but they were men who felt the men worked and brought home the bacon, and the ladies kept the house and cooked the bacon. They desperately wanted to take care of us, not the other way around. With all of us now looking, it appeared as if they felt like failures. Carmen and I saw it as quite the opposite, we were very pleased to lend a helping hand to our gallant knights.

As we crossed the street, a rather short pudgy man with a distinct duck walk and "Crusty the Clown" mannerism took a rather abrupt U turn in the middle of the intersection as a police car turned the corner. He began walking right along with us as if we were long time buddies from the old country.

"Whew," he commented "I wouldn't want to run into them."

I didn't know who he was talking about, but I didn't want to ask, either. This "old guy" looked like a "dork", one of those people who you don't know but they want to talk to you about anything and in anyway, if you let him. He didn't act right, maybe he was homeless, we wondered. He was wearing slacks and a short-sleeved shirt that was left un-tucked. His hair was neatly combed back, in the 1950's greaser rack-it-back style. He was not attractive in the least and both Carmen and I tried to get rid of him as politely as we could.

"So, what's going on?" He asked as if inviting himself to tag along.

"Nothing, just looking around." We answered.

Carmen and I had the same thought "Go away, old guy"

But he just didn't get it. He followed us wherever we went. We just couldn't shake him no matter what we said.

"Well!" I finally announced, "Maybe we ought to try tomorrow."

Carmen picked up on what I was saying "Yeah, maybe if we come out earlier tomorrow, we can hit more places."

The guy acted as if he didn't even hear us. "So, are you all working?"

"No," replied Carmen, "We're looking for work, but we are going to go back to our hotel room right now."

Again, he didn't appear even to hear us.

"I guess I should introduce myself, huh!" He excitedly announced "I'm Bobby. What's yer names?"

We didn't want to give him our real names for some unknown reason, maybe it was the whole "We're in the city now, blah, blah, blah." Whatever the reason I said my name was "Gloria Swanson". I had heard the name somewhere, but I did not realize she was a famous actress. Bobby snickered but didn't say anything. Carmen, seeing his reaction to my "infamous" name said "I'm Carmen."

I felt totally betrayed and extremely embarrassed at the same time. I decided well, if Carmen was willing to give her real name, I would too.

"My name isn't really Gloria, it's Kim." I awkwardly confessed.

"I didn't think Gloria was your real name." he replied with a "You are so busted" look on his face.

After suggesting we would go back to the hotel, we decided we were not going to be able to get rid of this guy while we were out. Our only recourse was to go back to the room like we said. There we knew we could keep him from following us.

Each day we went out in search of a job and each day our confidence in finding one dwindling a little bit more. By the fourth day, we were depressed and hungry, we probably looked more like we were begging than looking for gainful employment. Each day we tried to find something and each day, there was Bobby. It was a little creepy how he always seems to find us once we left the hotel. We were beginning to think rudeness was our only hope of getting rid of this irritating guy, when out of the blue he said,

"Are you girls hungry? I'm hungry."

Do our ears deceive us? Did he just ask if we wanted something...to...EAT??!"

We felt bad for trying to get rid of him as we accepted his invitation, but we had gone a week now surviving on only water and Tang.

Within just a couple of days, we found ourselves beginning to rely on ol' "Crusty" to always be there and to feed us, but I was still a bit more leery of him than Carmen.

Matt had given me a beautiful pistol for protection when I explained it was strange that he would spend money on us without wanting anything in return. It didn't help. I had carefully tucked it into my purse however, even before we were seated in the booth, he knew I had something. Bobby appeared to be shifting his body to get comfy when he suddenly reached over the table, took my purse and was looking through it. Somehow, he knew I had a gun and he wanted it.

"Girl, you shouldn't be carrying this around. You never know what will happen, you could get yourself killed!" He did not make any effort to hide it as he admired the 22-caliber silver finished pistol. The handgrip was stunning with the ornately carved Mother-of-Pearl. It was obvious he admired it, because he then simply tucked it in his belt under his shirt.

"Hey, give that back!" I argued.

He calmly replied "Nope, do you know what you want to eat?"

"I want my pistol back!" again I protested.

"You're not getting it back." he insisted. I knew then it was futile to try any farther and I wasn't getting any assistance from my "friend", which made me even madder.

"I don't want anything to eat!" I said copping my 17-year-old attitude.

Bobby was more than willing to oblige me, but Carmen knew it was our only meal

"Come on Kim, you haven't eaten all day!"

But I have a stubborn streak. "No, I'm fine!" I insisted.

I sat there refusing to order anything but a cup of coffee that is until the waitress brought all that food to the table. Bobby had a big juicy cheeseburger. It had lettuce and beautifully ripened tomato slices.

Catsup and mustard oozed out when he took his first slow, savoring bite. The burger seeped a glistening juice that was on his fingers of which he dutifully licked off one savory finger at a time.

I looked over to Carmen as she dipped her lightly browned, crisp and perfectly round slice of battered onion goodness into the thick mound of House brand catsup. The aroma of their burgers and onion rings would have been too much for any staunch meat eater there was.

"Okay" I blurted "if it's still okay, I would like to eat." Again, I had embarrassed myself, but he was happy to oblige and called the waitress back.

Before I knew it, Bobby had "pulled" Carmen and had just as fast turned her out, I was separated from Matt and Bear who were consequently threatened with their lives and mine, if they didn't leave the city and leave me and Carmen there with him. They couldn't even come find us to say good-bye. Bobby just put them on a bus back home, telling me that Matt and Bear ran off without a thought about me or Carmen, but I knew. I knew they would be back just as soon as they could. I also knew that neither one of them would have ever abandoned us as Bobby said. I just knew Bob must have threatened them.

After talking, flashing thick rolls of cash, and having Carmen show off her new clothes he got her, Bobby finally got fed up of me telling him that I would not sell my body and told me to take my "High and mighty, self-absorbed, selfish" attitude and leave.

"Go on, get out of here!" He barked.

"Where am I supposed to go?" I blurted out without even thinking.

"I don't give a shit!"

Carmen had new clothes, money, and an apartment. Everything we were looking for in a life in Chicago. I found myself homeless with nowhere to turn. With a hopelessly alone in the world feeling deep within my gut and mind, I walked to the beach. I don't know what I was expecting to see or get from the still water, maybe just some quiet privacy to allow those defeated tears to fall. I sat on a bench, considering what I could do. I was at a dead-end with nothing and no one there. I had felt low before, but never as defeated as I felt at that very moment. I thought I had no choice.

My options included sleeping on the beach not knowing where my next meal would come from or finding Bob and surrender to his style of life. A life I never in my wildest dreams would have thought I would have to live.

I grew up in a privileged house. Everything I needed was provided. Not necessarily, what I wanted but I was provided with what I needed. I was a Christian or so I thought...So how could I have possibly gotten myself into such a mess? I wasn't like those girls walking the streets, I wasn't even loose, in fact, I had barely lost my virginity.

Am I acting all high and mighty like he said? Am I self-absorbed, selfish? I wanted Carmen to come back with me but that would put her right back where I was at that moment!

I was lost, totally alone and I felt cornered. Bob had told me that Matt and Bear had left me that they didn't care about me and decided to go back home. In essence, he was telling me they had "abandoned" me because they didn't care what happened to me. No one cared but he would be willing to take me in.

I didn't want to do what Carmen was doing. I DON'T WANT TO...BE...a prostitute.... I'm a good girl.

I'm a good girl.

Chapter 8

I felt like I was crawling back on my hands and knees and asking forgiveness for my inconsiderate, albeit honest, behavior. I expected to be pushed away however, I was surprised he welcomed me in. The next day Bobby took me shopping for a couple of outfits better fitting to my new occupation.

I hadn't seen Carmen since talking to Bobby then when I asked where she was, he simply said "Out working. Don't worry about her, let's get you set."

But I did worry.

"Bobby, can I see Carmen?"

"I sold her" Was his reply then turning to me in a loving way he went on "I really didn't want her," pulling me up to him in an admiring hold. "It was you I wanted the whole time. I thought if she came than you might come too."

I was devastated. My best friend, my ONLY friend in the world and now she is gone.

"Can we visit each other?" My unexpected question was sternly avoided. I did not pursue it any further.

When we finished our shopping, DeeDee, Bobby's supposed wife had joined us to go get something to eat. Making our way to Bobby's car, he began to instruct me on the why's and wherefores of his "ladies" way of life I would have preferred not to be in. My head began to swirl with all the information that he was throwing at me.

"Get the money first," He said "Never afterward"

"Hide the money where the trick doesn't know where it is. Understand?"

"Never, ever" Bobby stressed "never, give the money back under any circumstance. Understand, if he gets a room ask him if you can keep the key, understand? So, you can use it the rest of the night. Understand?... understand?... understand?" On and on he went, how to check for the clap, understand? How to avoid police, understand? How much to get and for what, understand? Straight, head, half-and-half. I wanted to ask him to explain but thought if I did, I'd look stupid. I can't tell you why, but I also had the feeling that I shouldn't question Bobby. A strong feeling that the word "Why" was not in his girls' vocabulary when it came to be told what to do.

The three of us arrived at the little cafe where Bobby led us to a booth by the window that looked out on to the street. A busy, yet barren cafe. Everything seemed a little greasy, dirty and incredibly old. Even the maroon seat cushions were split in various areas and collapsed down so when you sat in one of the collapsed spots you sunk down to the height of a four-year-old. There was a bar that faced the long kitchen against the back wall, where you could watch the hefty woman in a hair

net and filthy white apron frying hamburgers, fries, and sautéing onions. Bobby sat with his arms crossed on the table. I noticed a spot of jelly next to his right elbow...no, that would be HIS left elbow. Bob was talking to DeeDee, I was trying to listen, but that spot of jelly had me wondering if our table had even been washed off. Neither DeeDee nor Bobby seemed to notice, and I didn't say anything.

When the waitress came to the table, Bobby sat back with one arm over the back of the broken-down seat and the other propping him up in what would become known as a gangster lean. Tatiana, our waitress asked what we would like as she began wiping the jelly off the table.

After we ordered, Bobby turned in my direction as he began to talk about what I was to expect, especially what I could count on him for.

"I work, too." He said with a smile. "I'm always close by and watching you just in case you get a bad trick."

I glanced at DeeDee who didn't seem to be fazed by any of his words. Personally, I believed him and was very happy that he would do that for us even though I did not think we could have such a trick. DeeDee never even looked up from her pop.

We sat quietly as the waitress brought our food and set each plate down in front of us. She smiled and asked if we needed anything else

"Mayonnaise?" DeeDee said.

"No problem, I'll be right back."

But before she could return with the little paper cup with mayo, Bobby, who was now looking out the window anxiously announced "DeeDee! Isn't that one of your regulars?"

My eyes naturally went out the window even though I had no idea who the spotted regular could be. DeeDee quickly looked up and asked "Where? Where?"

"Right, THERE!" he said, "Isn't that one of yours?" he asked obviously becoming agitated as DeeDee frantically looked up and down the street.

"Go!" Bob demanded.

I wondered if this was commonplace with him. Does he do this sort of thing a lot? DeeDee obediently and a little confused jumped out of her seat and ran to the door.

I was amazed that she wasn't even given time to eat her lunch before she was sent out to turn a trick. But up she went and disappeared around the corner of the building. I wondered if I was ever going to have to do something like that.

I asked about her food, but he didn't seem to be worried about it.

I wonder now if it was all show to let me know never to question him.

"Have you ever given anyone some head?" Bobby asked.

I had never heard that term and my thoughts went all over the place. I knew it must be some sort of sexual act, but I did not have a clue. "Head, head" my mind searched. I had images of rubbing my head into the guy's belly. He must have seen my confusion after a moment of silence.

"A blow job." He clarified.

"WOW!!" I was taken aback. It was a disgusting thought, let alone an act on someone I don't even know. I understood a little bit, but as far as how to perform this act, I hadn't the foggiest idea. I felt embarrassed for how little I knew about sex. My father thought if we didn't know, we wouldn't do, so he had told my mom not to talk about it to us. So, in the infamous words of Gomer Pyle, from the 1960's sitcom Gomer Pyle: USMC: "SUE-PRISE, SUE-PRISE, SUE-PRISE." I'm sure Dad never thought I'd get into a mess like this.

He wanted to demonstrate how to do it, on a couple of my fingers want when he told me this, I looked around the cafe in absolute shock! He just laughed and said not here, he would show me later.

"Just act like he's the greatest boyfriend you ever had, and you'll be great!" Bobby said.

Bob had someone he had made a deal with, he would set him up with a first time turn out for $10.00 and in return, the trick would report back to Bobby with how they acted. He was my first trick. All he told me was he had a trick for me to "turn" and he was a nice guy. He told me his name, but I was so terrified I promptly forgot it. I followed procedure as I was told and when it was over, I just laid there with a man I did not know. I just didn't know what to do...or say for that matter, so I laid there. When he got up, I was so happy it was over and even happier that I didn't get sick all over him.

Later that evening Bobby explained his arrangement with this young man. I had mixed feelings of disgust, shock, and embarrassment because it was as if Bobby was watching me do this thing.

The following day, Bobby came into the apartment and announced to us that we were going to New Orleans. Everyone was so excited and since I had never seen New Orleans, I was just as excited as anyone else. We packed and were on the road inside of one hour. DeeDee sat in the front since she was "number-one", she was also legally married to Bobby. Being number-one meant she had the highest status of all the girls. She was trusted more, but with the trust came more responsibility, like going to the bus station to help pull a new girl.

Bobby had a new Cadillac, white with plush overstuffed leather seats. It was gorgeous and I felt honored to be sitting in it. Everything was electric, even the steering wheel! I had never ridden in such a fancy car before now. I sunk down into the seat and stretched my legs as far as I could without bothering Jolene who was sitting on the other side of the back seat. She sneered at me because I took such liberty. She would never speak to me unless it was in anger.

When we arrived in New Orleans, it was about four in the afternoon. Bob asked if we were hungry. The little cafe was very indigenous to the city and its people. The table we sat down at had a cushioned seat similar to those in a booth, however, the opposite side provided chairs instead of the booth seat. I wanted to sit in the booth side facing the dining room, but Bobby informed me that he always sat so he could see the door and DeeDee was who sat next to him.

DeeDee had never tried authentic seafood gumbo and in New Orleans, you never know what you're going to find in it. Bobby teased her saying there was fish heads as well as whatever the cook wanted to put in it.

"Crawdads, fish heads, beetles, maybe a cockroach or two." He teased. "You never know what you'll find in New Orleans Gumbo.

They call it Gumbo because they used to put dirt and rocks in it. If I was you, I might want to check it out very careful before I ate it."

When her soup came, she took her spoon and began cautiously examining her soup. She gingerly moved each individual unidentifiable vegetable and strangely suspicious piece of seafood in the brown liquid when suddenly, Bobby screamed and knocked into DeeDee who simultaneously jumped and she flip her spoon and bowl full of never before tasted concoction aptly named "gumbo" into the next booth and on to the table and floor. She got it all over our table and her lap. Bobby laughed so hard I thought for sure he was going to have to change his britches. However, I wasn't sure if it was okay to laugh or not because Bobby sounded like he got mad with his scream. Jolene thought it was hilarious and joined in the laughing making me feel comfortable enough to smile at DeeDee's mishap. DeeDee, on the other hand, did not look very happy as she sat there looking down at her seafood gumbo covered lap.

I was sincerely bummed when we were told we needed to get to work. Bobby took DeeDee aside to talk to her and then disappeared. When I asked where he went, DeeDee simply, but authoritatively answered

"He's around"

I really wanted to explore the French Quarter. There were bands playing jazz inside of bars and eateries. Some didn't even have a wall going out onto the street.

"They're probably open 24 hours." DeeDee told me. "But that's not why we're here, come on."

It was almost like she turned into a mini-Bobby. Her attitude toward me was always horrible, but this was definitely a "stop asking questions!" order. I didn't believe she was any better than I was, anyway, I wanted to explore the culture and arts of the Creole people, so I continued asking questions and...

"Awe, can't we just check this band out for a few?"

"NO!"

"Wow," I thought "She sounded just like Bobby did when I asked a favor."

She insisted that we were going to work and that was that. She ignored my questions after that.

"Man, what a party pooper." I thought to myself as I reluctantly followed "Little Miss Mini-Bobby."

I was rather disappointed when we got to the bar we were to work. It was nothing like Bourbon Street with the excitement and culture. It was like going from captivating to colorless. There were no smiles! No excitement or celebrating. There were only dull, dreary, true to form alcoholics in unkempt clothing and their five o'clock shadows, hunched over their prized glass of booze. It was almost like they were protecting that half of an ounce from would be thieves out to reform the boozing cretin.

Not knowing what I was doing, I assumed we were going to sit at one of the tables. I headed for one, but Mini-Bobby said rather drolly, "You have to sit at the bar." When I asked why she said, "Because you have to." I went to follow Jolene and DeeDee, who headed for the bottom of the "L" shaped table lined with small round stools but was quickly informed that I was not to sit with them. I assumed we were to all sit apart, but I was the only one that was not invited.

I sat by myself for a brief moment, not having a clue as to where to start.

"Well," I told myself "I might as well see if they will tell me anything."

I casually strolled over to the pair and asked what I was supposed to do to get a trick.

Trick...trick...an interesting word to describe a person who is looking for a prostitute. It felt strange using the word "trick," I wonder if the term came from the idea of TRICKING a person to think she wants him and him alone.

DeeDee said "Order a drink and when someone comes in ask him if he wants a "date".

Another interesting term. "date" Must mean to "have sex for money" I certainly don't think it means the same as it did in high school.

I asked what I should do if he says he is interested, she said "nothing! Just find out how much he wants to spend and for what." DeeDee then turned her attention on Jolene who hadn't said a word. DeeDee was not extremely helpful because I was still very confused and unsure of myself. I was getting the feeling that she and Jolene didn't like me very much.

"How much should I ask for?"

"I DON'T KNOW!" was the rather curt reply.

I glanced at Jolene for any help, but she just looked at me like I was a moldy piece of raw fish stinking up her area.

"Well, I guess I can't depend on them for help." I thought. "I'll just have to figure things out on my own."

Sitting on the stool, I watched Jolene approach someone however, it was a no go. He must not have been interested.

I took a sip of my drink, it was horrible, and my face showed it. The bartender had told me I had to order an alcoholic drink. I was not a drinker and had no experience with any hard liquor. The bartender whispered to me to order a rum and coke. He would carefully pour the rum on the top and if I drank from the small straw, I would only get pop, unfortunately, I could still taste the nasty stuff. I set it down hoping I wouldn't have to drink the whole thing.

As I sat on the stool feeling very ignorant, I heard a quiet voice say, "Umm, excuse me miss." I turned to see a young boy, probably about my age. I smiled and answered him "Yes?"

"Umm..." his inexperience came through loud and clear. "Umm, well...we, uh, my friends and I, I mean," he was almost cute the way he stumbled for the right words. "Well...we were wondering if you were a real prostitute."

I felt just as uncomfortable admitting to being one.

"Well, my friends and I are here on vacation and would like to proposition you. I drew the short straw."

He was basically a good-looking guy and a trick is a trick. I asked where his friends were, and he pointed behind him. There stood six more young guys, all about the same age. They were huddled together with the same wide grin that my first shy fellow had. I smiled back and the group of first timers all waved at once. It felt bazaar and probably looked hilarious, a first-time hooker with seven first time tricks all waving across the old grungy bar of experience.

We eventually got the particulars straight and I went over to DeeDee to ask if they wanted to come along to help since there were so many of them. DeeDee about had hit the roof. She angrily told me they were trouble and that I had better get rid of them before we all were busted.

This angered me because I felt she was being unreasonable. She hadn't been willing to coach me in the ways of prostitution, and now she was saying that these naive young first timers may be cops, and if they weren't cops, they were definitely trouble.

"They're not cops, they said they had never done this before and wanted to try it out."

Now Jolene chimed in telling me that I didn't know what I was getting myself into echoing DeeDee's comment that they were just "kids".

"Well, I think they are fine and I'm going to take them to the room." I barked back "Do you want to come or not!"

"NO!" was their combined answer.

"Fine!"

I was very sure to tell them not to walk with me but to meet me at the motel and I would be there. Bobby had told me never to let more than one in the room at a time. So, when we meet at the hotel, I said.

"Only one at a time, the rest of you need to wait at the bottom of the steps."

The steps went from the back-parking lot to the second-floor landing where my room was.

"It's the first room to the left," I explained. Then I laid the law down to my young recruits. "You have to stay at the bottom of the steps and only one of you can be in the room at a time, so when the first guy is done, he will go and get someone else." I wanted to sound very stern so they would follow my instructions. They happily agreed and I went upstairs with the first trick I actually got myself.

He handed me the $25.00 we agreed on and we got undressed.

About halfway through there was a knock on the door.

"That better not be one of your friends!" I said threateningly.

"It shouldn't be." He replied.

I went to the door and crouched close. "Who is it?" I asked.

It was Bobby.

"Kim? Are you okay?" he asked as if he was talking to a three-year-old.

"I'm fine." I replied in the same tone.

"How many are in there with you?"

I answered, "Just one"

Bobby told me to talk to him when we finished and I agreed, wondering what the problem was.

When I went back to my trick, he asked if that was my pimp and if everything was okay. "Oh, sure." I said, "We're fine, I'm going to meet him at the bar when we finish."

As I opened the door to let Mr. Number One out to get Mr. Number Two, I saw that Bobby was sitting with my young cavaliers as if he was waiting for his turn. I just smiled and he sat there chatting with the guys until they were all done.

Bobby was laughing so hard he was actually tearing, "DeeDee and Jo said that you had taken a bunch of kids up to the room and you were in there with all of them!" he explained. "Well, I come bustin' ass over here expecting to find a gang-bang going on."

Even though he was laughing, I was a bit nervous because I did not know what to expect from him.

"Well, when I got here, I almost fell right over the whole group of them. I asked them if they were waiting for you and you know what they said?" laughing almost hysterically, "They said I had to wait my turn because only one was aloud in the room at a time! I had to wait. ME!"

"They were right there on the steps?!" I said with as much shock as I could muster up. Truthfully, I was more afraid of what Bob would do than the idea that my young dates were not sitting where I had told them to. "I told them they had to wait at the bottom of the steps until it was their turn," He didn't seem to hear me, so I repeated, "I told them to stay at the bottom of the stairs." I wanted Bobby to know that they were not to be sitting at the top of the steps so close to the room.

I wasn't really sure he ever heard me over his own laughter that I felt a quick giggle escape my own lips.

Bob told that story over and over again bragging to his fellow "managers" about his new ho. He also included how his main ho chased him down to tell on me, there by prompting his mad dash to the motel.

His turnout bagged seven baby tricks her first time out. None of his seasoned girls would help her, so she took them all on, leaving the experienced girls behind to find their own tricks. Well if DeeDee and Jolene didn't like me before, they really hated me now.

Bobby laughed and reviewed the scene over and over again, as we headed out of New Orleans. Bobby had given me the honored spot in the front seat with him. Jo and DeeDee fumed and never said a word the entire trip back to Chicago.

Soon after arriving in Chicago, reality set in and we were expected to work the streets. Even after New Orleans, I felt very insecure and really did not know what to do but I did not want to ask DeeDee, not after everything that had happened. Unfortunately, I didn't have a choice. She was my only source of training. We typically only saw Bob once a day, at the end of our night so he could pick up the money we had made and take us out to breakfast.

Jolene couldn't handle it and ran off in the middle of the night. Bobby didn't seem to care one way or another, his opinion was that she was jealous of me and did not like her new status of number three. DeeDee was still number one of course, but I had taken the number two spot over. New Orleans put me there.

Even though I really didn't know her, it felt strange not having Jolene with us. DeeDee was there to stay and I knew that, still I felt vulnerable with Jolene gone. I couldn't tell you why, I just didn't like the feeling it gave me.

Chapter 9

I asked DeeDee if we could work together. I was feeling insecure on this whole street thing. I told her I wanted to get some pointers from watching her getting tricks. Truthfully, I was scared shitless that I would make a mistake or wouldn't be able to find one and have Bobby to deal with. This must have given her pride a boost, because she agreed to help me and was actually willing to talk to me. Mostly I had to prompt any conversation, but she talked! I felt a ray of hope pop through. Maybe, just maybe, we could be friends.

I needed a friend, someone I could talk to, confide in, someone that liked me enough to say, "You're my friend." I had not had many friends growing up, but there was always at least one friend in my life, until now. DeeDee made no bones about her disdain for me, and as for Bob, well, no friend would treat another friend the way he treats us. He said he cares and that he loves me, but it all seems to depend on how much money we each bring in each night.

"I'm hungry." We had only been up since noon, but I had not gotten anything to eat before we left.

"I ..." Her smug tone carried a message of superiority, "never eat before I turn my first trick."

A reminder of her dislike for me that I was not all that thrilled to receive. However, I thought I should make the best of it and find a way to compliment her personal discipline.

"Is that how you stay so skinny?"

That didn't go over very well...she picked up her pace to get ahead of and away from me. I truly did not understand why she was so angry. I thought it was a great compliment, but she thought I was referring to New Orleans or her "inability" to find tricks!

My stomach making so much noise that I just had to ask again.

"How about a little snack, just to get us through?" DeeDee, who was still trying to walk ahead of me, gave in and said we could get a little something, maybe a pop.

"Well, that will take the edge off." I thought sarcastically to myself.

"I don't have very much money, Bob took all the money last night." She said. "If you want more than that you will have to wait until you turn a trick."

"Excuse me, ladies." We turned and alongside the curb was the fanciest car I've ever seen. I looked at DeeDee and she looked at me.

"Excuse me, could I talk to you?" said the stranger.

We took a couple of steps forward before he stopped us.

"Sorry, I just need to talk to her." as he pointed directly at me. I looked at DeeDee who excitedly said, "Go, go!"

I walked up as I tried to muster all the calm confidence I could. I leaned down so I could see him better and asked, "Are you looking for a date?"

The man smiled and graciously declined. "Do you know who I am?"

"No," I answered.

"Well," he continued "Are you interested in modeling," I was taken aback. Not knowing what to say I turned down his offer. "Well, if you change your mind give me a call." and he reached his arm out and handed me a gold embossed card then he just smiled and drove off.

"Wha'd he want, wha'd he want?" DeeDee was jumping up and down clasping her hands. Her eyes also express her excitement. "WELL? Tell me!! Tell me!!" she was like a little child who had just been told her favorite aunt was coming to town.

"Awe, he said he wanted me to model for him." I answered, "A likely story, probably some guy lookin' for a freebie." And with that I tore up the card. I was trying to fit in, to appear as if I knew what I was doing.

"You IDIOT! THAT WAS HUGH HEFNER!!" She yelled as she extended her hand toward the street.

"Who's that?"

"He's only the richest man around and the owner of Playboy Magazine!"

"Oh"

The day was ridiculously hot, and the humidity was horrible, but with the excitement of Hugh Hefner, DeeDee didn't seem to notice. All she wanted to do was find Bob and tell him "HUGH HEFNER talked to us!"

When we found Bobby, DeeDee could hardly contain her emotions, she was jumping around as if she on hot coals trying to get him to understand what had happened. Bobby, trying to decipher her excited rambling caught a few words. "KIM...HEF...GOLD..." Bobby's eyes and mouth matched the look on DeeDee's face. I would have been laughing but I was a little nervous I was going to be in trouble for not going with him.

"HUGH HEFNER??? HUGH HEFNER wanted you to model for him?! Why didn't you go?!!" Bobby managed to get out.

"I thought he was just looking for a freebie."

Bobby grabbed the top of his head and threw himself back. "OH MY GOD! We could have had it made!"

DeeDee exclaimed "He even gave her a gold embossed business card...I bet it was REAL GOLD!"

All the excitement over this guy in a fancy car with a gold colored business card really shocked me. It didn't make any sense to me, he was just a guy.

Bobby began asking question after question hardly giving me time enough to answer and then... he wanted to see the card.

My heart leapt into my throat as I thought, "Oh, no, I tore it up, now he is really going to be mad."

"Where is it, you got his card? Let me see it. Call him, give him a call see what he says!!!"

"Bob, Bob" DeeDee interrupted "She tore it up."

Silence, dead silence, then.

"You...tore...it...UP???" Bobby asked even more shocked.

I opened my mouth to explain why I tore it up, but only a squeaky "yes." managed to come out. Then the laughter began. Bobby had another great story to tell his cronies while waiting for the nights take. One of his ho's turned Hugh Hefner down and even tore up his card. Of course, the story would be embellished with lies to make him look better.

We learned sometime later that I resembled Hugh Hefner's first wife when she was my age.

I watched for that gold colored luxury car for many weeks before finally giving up.

Going out to work that steamy afternoon seemed to be senseless, no one in their right mind would be thinking about sex in this heat. The thermostat said it was 110° but that was up for debate. The heat even made breathing difficult in the shade! In the sun, it felt like an oven and that old cliché. "It is so hot you can fry an egg on the sidewalk..." is not just a cliché, I'm telling you it is a fact! I know because we tried it out! While the egg was cooking sunny side up, Bobby suggested we get a steak and fry that up, too.

"Come on, girls, there are no tricks out today."

Bobby decided we were going to go somewhere that had air conditioning and cool off. DeeDee and I couldn't have been happier because not only was the heat excruciatingly hot, but the humidity was busting through the meter...

We walked into the apartment, I took one look and asked, "What's that?" With a rather hefty amount of shock. Apparently neither one of them understood what I was talking about so with both hands opened and aimed towards the wall, I exclaimed "THE WALL'S ARE DRIPPING!!"

"That is the humidity."

By the time we had cleaned up and changed out of our work clothes, we were soaked in sweat again. There was nothing we could do to avoid it, so we just got into the car.

Inside the car was even hotter than outside in the sun, but it didn't take long before I could feel the cool breeze of the air conditioner touch the hot droplets on my face. I closed my eyes so I could pull its coolness along one side of my face and then the next side. The cool air felt like tiny downy feathers brushing the heat from my cheeks, cooling me as it moved around the inside of the car. I took a deep cleansing breath and stretched from one door to the other. We were all soaking in the cool air so much that we were totally unaware of the unmarked squad cars positioning themselves to perform a covert sting.

Just that quick, five vehicles surrounded the three of us. They screeched into position making escape impossible. Two of them stopped only yards from our front end, one alongside us, a fourth jumped the curb blocking the westward escape over a vacant lot and a final car landed at a 200° angle across our rear end in a Dominic Toretto's "Fast and Furious" drift.

Bobby slammed on the brakes and turned into the curb to avoid what looked to be an inevitable head-on collision. From the surrounding vehicles, numerous men leapt out brandishing pistols and shouting, "POLICE, OUT'TA THE CAR! HANDS ON YOUR HEADS!"

Instinctively, Bobby threw his hands up over the dash board in surrender before one of the men with a pistol aimed right at him, quickly yet cautiously, threw the driver side door open, stepped back again and in what has been referred to as the Police Isosceles Stance held his aim on Bobby shouting orders

"LEM'ME SEE YER HANDS, NOW!! MOVE, OUT'TA THE VEHICLE, NOW, NOW!"

Bobby obediently placed his hands over his head and got out of the car.

"ON THE GROUND, ON THE GROUND, NOW, MOVE IT!" The plain clothed cop roared and again, Bobby complied with the officer's orders.

"DON'T MOVE, STAY DOWN." The officer shouted orders as he knelt down and put his knee into Bob's back. He then pulled Bob's arms back and handcuffed him as another stood a few feet away with the barrel of his pistol aiming right at the back of Bob's head. "DON'T MOVE, I DON'T WANT TO SEE YOU EVEN FLINCH!"

While that was going on with Bobby, DeeDee and I were hustled out of the passenger's side of the car at gunpoint.

"COME ON, OUT'TA THE CAR." They were demanding but not as sharply with us as they were with Bobby. Similarly, we were not ordered to the ground or handcuffed like Bobby.

With all the screeching and spinning vehicles, police yelling orders over each other, and irons brandished everywhere you looked confusion as to why this was happening just added to the well-orchestrated disorder.

I knew to keep my mouth shut if I didn't want screamed at, humiliated, or beat, not by the police, you understand, I was afraid of Bobby. I did, however lean toward DeeDee and whisper, "What's going on?"

"We're going to jail." She said in the pompous tone she typically took with me.

"But why did they stop us?" I asked still in a state of confusion.

DeeDee was just as bewildered as I was for the Bonny and Clyde style of arrest. She did however know it was much more than a "loitering" charge. "I don't know!" She snapped, "Just shut up and... LOOK OUT!"

I saw her flip around to hide her face, I followed suit even though I didn't know why. DeeDee looked up after a moment and told me it was okay. I took her lead then asked, "What happened?"

"The newspaper photographer was trying to take our picture."

I looked around to find the photographer who seemed to have vanished into thin air. "Oh" I said, acknowledging her warning even though I didn't really understand what the big deal was. I didn't question her any farther than that because she could be just as nasty as Bobby when questioned, just without the hitting.

The photographer went around one of the police cars and snuck up behind Bobby.

By this time, they had decided to remove the cuffs from Bobby's wrists, most likely because the photographer wanted a good picture for the newspaper. "Let's see your money" One of the cops said, "So we know how much you have in case you lose it on the way to lock-up."

Pulling his cash out of his front pocket and fanned the massive number of bills on the car hood, Bobby suddenly caught sight of movement over his right shoulder. As if on cue, he threw his body over the fanned money and on to the hood thereby covering the bills and foiling all attempts of snapping a picture of the untaxed cash. Each time the photographer tried to capture the perfect candid image, he found his attempts thwarted...that is until…. our 'carriage' arrived and Bobby came up along the side of the paddy wagon. Again, DeeDee spotted the sneaky photographer as he was getting into position for one last attempt.

"Look out!" she warned. I didn't know quite where to turn, so I simply looked down at the street and towards DeeDee, but Bobby didn't hear her. As he looked up at us, he gestured and asked, "Are they coming with?"

-SNAP! - Front page news flash, a half page story, complete with a three inch by five-inch photograph of the three of us, "Prostitution Ring Arrested in Sting," immortalized for all eternity.

I had never seen a paddy wagon before but there it was, big as life.

"This is a paddy-wagon?!" I exclaimed as I was escorted up through the back. "I thought they were only in the days of Al Capone!"

Other than two small windows above the cab, our ride had no light, only metal benches in which to sit on. We took our seats and as I was looking around at the eight by ten mobile jail cell, Bobby warned "You better hang on as best as you can. They like to try and bump us around."

The first turn just about landed me in DeeDee's lap. As you can imagine, she wasn't very thrilled about it, but Bobby got a laugh out of it. He then began to tell me that this was nothing to worry about, it's no big deal.

"We pay the $25.00 bond and then we can go home." He explained. "Just be sure you don't tell them anything that could get me in trouble. Okay?"

He seemed rather relaxed as he lifted his foot to cross his knee and then using both arms to brace himself. I wasn't sure if I was that relaxed. DeeDee was sitting with her elbows on her knees, now. More than likely, she wanted to be sure that I wouldn't fall on her again. Maybe even hoping I would land on the floor.

He smiled at me again and said. "You busted your cherry, girl! First time." As the wagon made another sharp turn, Bobby was thrown off balance this time. We were being turned and twisted so violently that DeeDee had to grab hold of the bench as Bobby was thrown toward me. He had to grab a hold of my knee in an attempt to remain upright. Had he not been so quick with uncrossing his legs, he would have totally embarrassed himself, as he would have ended up on the floor. As it happened though, there may have been a small twinge of embarrassment bracing himself on my knee to keep his balance. He decided not to try to look so relaxed from then on.

We arrived at Cook County jail and were escorted, not to lock up, but to individual rooms. It didn't seem to be quite right, even Bobby was wondering what was up. One by one, a cop took us into a room and separately questioned us.

"Have a seat. Someone will be right in." the stoic cop said.

I looked around at my options as the cop closed the door behind him. There was one chair and a table. There was also a bench, which stretched the width of the room. I sat on the bench. It felt a bit arrogant for me to sit on the only chair in the room. I really do not know why, I guess it was my upbringing. Besides, I didn't want to be sitting in the chair if they brought a light in to shine in my eyes and "make me sing".

I imagined a "bad" cop circled me telling me to "CONFESS, we know you're the master mind! We KNOW you did it." With the good cop leaning over saying: "Just sign your name right here and I promise you ..." Then I'd say "SCREW YOU, COPPER. This gal isn't cracking"" I smiled at my comment to the imaginary cops, but it quickly disappeared

"Hello...Kim." A slightly pudgy man said as he walked into the room. After a bit, he glanced up from the folder he was carrying, and I returned the greeting.

"Hello"

He was bald but not completely bald, he did have some hair that circled the southern hemisphere of his head with a few strays that kept trying to stand upright. He seemed to have a nervous habit of running his hand over the top of his head as if he were smoothing the rogue stragglers that refused to lie down. It seemed to be a reaction in an uncomfortable situation, as if he felt uneasy about going bald. The same way a girl will tug at a skirt, she feels uncomfortable in because it's too short. He sat down and crossed his legs as he continued to look at the folder he was carrying.

"Is that me?" I asked

"Yes," he answered in a distant, "I'm thinking, leave me be." tone. He then slowly turned his head up towards me while keeping his eyes on the papers so he could finish reading those last few words.

When he did finally look up, I could tell that this was one guy who took pride in his job.

He was very stuffy and it would not have surprised me in the least, if when he was at home he liked to put on his smoking jacket and sit, cross-legged, in his favorite wing backed chair that he had purposely placed by the fireplace. Then with his faithful Irish Setter, Cecil, he smokes his Meerschaum pipe.

"Can I have a smoke?"
"No, this is a non-smoking building"
"Maaaan" I whined jokingly.

Scratching his bald spot again, he began asking me questions about who I was, how old I was, and what I did for a living, as well as, who the others were in my party.

"Hey," I interrupted "Aren't you going to put me under a light that shines down on me to make me "spill the beans"?"

"No, we don't do that, anymore." he replied with a bit of dry humor.

For three hours, I had answered the same questions over and over again. He would mix them up and ask the same question in various ways, but they were all the same question.

"What's your real name?"

"How old are you?"

"Who is Bobby and that other girl you were with?"

"Oh, come on..." I was really getting bored with the whole repetition thing. "You really have a one-track mind."

"Your ID says you're blond! Your hair is not a dye job."

"No, it's not, I let my real color grow back out." I answered.

"It says here, you have blue eyes."

"Colored contacts." I smiled

He sat back with a bit of frustration and challenged me for the truth. "You are not wearing contacts."

"Not now!"

He pushed his chair back, threw his hands up in utter frustration and said.

"You have all the answers, don't you?"

"Well... yeah." I answered in total adolescent ignorance.

My interrogator was so upset with me he got up and stormed out of the room.

When he didn't return, I wondered what was going on. I went over to the door that led out into the corridor just as Bobby was being led past. Seeing me peeking out of the window, He quickly mouthed "Did you tell?" I shook my head strongly from side to side mouthing back "NO!"

I found myself worrying now, wondering what the problem was. Bobby was worried what I might say to the police. I sat back down on the bench to wait for whatever was going to happen next. A few moments later, a younger man came into the room. Not only was this new cop not stuffy like the first, but he actually smiled. He introduced himself as Frank and shook my hand. No one had ever shaken my hand before...it felt strange. I felt as if he respected me and in return, I felt more relaxed talking to him.

"Hi, Kim. How are you doing?"

"Now this guy is a lot nicer than that other fella." I thought

"I'm great, how about you?" I answered. He said that he was also great and that he thought we ought to just sit down and get to know each other a little bit.

We chit-chatted for a bit and the conversation gradually moved over to what they knew to be true about me, where I grew up, my dad's name, phone number and address. It totally amazed me, and I thought, "Okay, the gig is up. No sense in trying to tell him he was wrong."

"Why didn't you want to tell Officer Banner?"

"He wasn't a nice guy." I answered.

Frank replied, "Yeah, that guy really is kind of...full of himself." Then he leaned in close to me and said, "I don't care for him either."

Frank had told me he was not a policeman, nor did he work for the Cook County Police Department. He did not tell me he was in the narcotics division and that he was one of big wigs they send into people they couldn't "crack"!

Frank pulled his chair closer to me and with a quick glance to the door he looked me square in the eyes and whispered "Tell me something, Kim..."

"Yeah?" I leaned in and whispered back.

It would be our little secret. Just between the two of us. No one else would know.

"Did you, Bob or DeeDee have any heroin, or coke in the car when you got busted?"

I was really shocked that he was asking that, and I wondered why he was whispering, but he was so captivatingly nice, I whispered back my answer.

"No..."

Frank winked "Aw, you can tell me. The guy you were with, he had the drugs, right?"

I sat up "No. We really didn't"

"Really?"

"Really, nothing, I don't even do drugs." I assured him.

Well, that was the end of our friendship. Frank got up and brazenly walked out. The friendly conversation we were having was dropped flat, without so much as a "Check ya' later, Bitch"

I felt tricked, out conned, taken for a fool, and I was angry with myself for letting this crack-shot detective get to me. I thought we were getting along great! However, he's just doing his job of play-acting with the whore. I had frustrated the first cop, but this one had gotten the information he was looking for and it had only taken five, maybe ten minutes.

-Bastard-

I was so disappointed in myself for being shanghaied by his friendly and understanding charm. This guy was able to get me to tell him what he wanted to know by merely acting as if he wanted to be my friend. In those few minutes, he learned who I was and what I was, although not the information he was hoping for, but information, nonetheless. I had been duped and it would not happen again.

Chapter 10

"There's a cop known as Big Jim." DeeDee warned me. "And he's the best vice there is and if he sees you, you're going to jail for sure. So just be careful." Bobby picked up the discussion from there and said that Big Jim has busted every lady in the entire eighteenth district, which encompassed most of the near north side of Chicago.

Because of that picture of us in that newspaper article, I was tagged, it was as if someone slapped a paper on my back that said "Hooker".

DeeDee explained deeper, "With that article and picture, "prostitution crackdown", you had been identified as a "known street prostitute" and are now subject to being arrested whenever you are spotted.

I had been put out on my own now, no more sharing "the stro" so to speak. It was the way Bobby wanted it. We went out alone, tricked our own, and if busted we were on our own.

"You, there," I heard a low baritone voice. "Come'ear,"

Crap!

I pointed to myself and said "Me?" as innocently as I could.

He snickered "Yeah...you."

I bound over to him knowing I was going to go to jail, and I could do nothing about it.

"What's yer name?"

Deciding to have a little fun, I replied, "Kim, what's yours?"

"Well, you lovely ladies and your men know me as Big Jim"

"BIG JIM!?" I acted as if he was a celebrity. "WOW, I've heard all about you."

Our conversation went on for a bit as he escorted me over to his vice-car. I was surprised at how polite and even respectful he seemed. He referred to me as a "lady" and Bobby as "my man" instead of whore and pimp. He never even once spoke down to me or accused me of being less than human. He was great fun to kid because he kidded right back.

Most of the time I was busted it was by Big Jim. I wondered at the time if it was coincidence or if it was by design. Whatever the reason, the objective was never to have to withstand a three-hour interrogation again, so I just had fun with it.

Big Jim made it easy.

It became another part of the job. No one thought I took going to jail serious, but I did take it serious, serious enough to make light of it so I wouldn't be harassed, and I wouldn't be questioned for hours.

I liked to tell him I had been looking all over town for him, or that I had missed him. Once when he called my name out, I gave him a big tooth smile and a twinkling eye as I ran up to him with my arms out to give him a hug. I stopped short and held out my hand to shake his. "How do you do, officer. Can I assist you in any way?" He smiled as he opened the door to his squad car for me to get in. "Yes, ma'am, you can make yourself comfortable as we chauffeur you downtown."

"Oh, my." I responded as a queen would to her intended, "Thank you sir"

Eventually, Big Jim wouldn't even get out of the car. He would just call me by name and tell me to get in the car.

Big Jim was aptly nicknamed with his tall and stout frame. His face had almost a soft look to it, but it showed a slight bit of wear. Probably from all the evil he had experienced and seen in his career.

"Hey, why don't I just climb in the back seat with you and we'll have a little fun." Big Jim said.

"With ME?!" I followed, "Why, what would your friend say?"

"Eh, he's the quiet type. He won't say anything."

Flirting or simply having fun, Big Jim had always left me with a "See ya' next time" The other cops just treated me with disgust.

"Kim!" The familiar voice of Big Jim called to me once again.

"Aww, man, I was just going to get something to eat. I'm starved," I said as my stomach grumbled at me.

"Come on, Kim, we'll stop by McDonalds."

It was such a wonderful gesture. I had never heard of this happening before.

"Wow, really?" I asked very shocked.

"Yeah, we'll go." His partner looked at Big Jim with an expressionless "WHAT?!!" in his eyes. Jim didn't pay any attention to his young rookie driver but added, "Just don't expect it every time."

I was so thrilled a cop would do that for me. I felt, although he was taking me to jail for illegally renting my body out, that that show of consideration and respect would never go forgotten. He showed me that there was hope for me, yet. Maybe I wasn't the disgusting whore that I appear to be.

I was rapidly losing faith in humanity and I didn't even realize it.

It was about one o'clock in the morning when we arrived at lock up. Big Jim put on his cop face and escorted me through the back door.

"Didn't you say I would be a guest of the county?" I asked. "Shouldn't we go through the front door then?" Big Jim just snickered and said, "Nope, you're a back-door kind of guest."

As he brought me to the booking desk, I felt a twinge of depression come over me and I wished he wouldn't leave. But he did, and I was left standing. The woman behind the desk looked at me rather annoyed. I decided she wasn't up for any bantering. The woman took down my name and allowed me my one call, provided I had the twenty-five cents to feed the pay phone.

After my "one" call to Bobby, I was rather rudely escorted to a semi-secluded room. The walls were a blah-grey colored concrete reminded me of the shower room at my old high school. The floor dipped slightly toward the center where it connected with a drain. I suspected it was to ensure any liquid would find its proper home. I really didn't care to think about what type of liquid it might be. I then wondered if they planned on "delicing" me. I had seen it in a movie where they then scrubbed the person with hard bristled brushes.

"Okay, strip!"

"Strip?" I asked in surprise.

"Yeah, that's right, missy" the head matron answered, "Strip, just like you have many times for your tricks."

"That was uncalled for" I had to bite the inside of my cheek to keep from telling this ugly witch how rude she was being.

Interestingly I actually found myself a bit modest undressing in front of these women. One of them made a rude comment referring to my modesty as being a tall tale. I sneered at their disrespect.

"Arm's out," she barked like a cold fish while I stood naked in front of them.

"Stand with your legs apart." she continued. "Open your mouth!"

"Stick your tongue out." I thought about giving her the raspberries but decided I had better not. "Move your tongue side to side and up and down." She came close as she inspected the inside of my mouth for contraband, then…

"Turn around, bend over and spread your butt cheeks."

It only takes a cough or sneeze to fart in 2015 but not in 1975, too bad.

When the three dykes were satisfied, I wasn't hiding anything, the matron who hadn't spoken a word directed me to come with her. She led me down past a few cells positioning herself between the wall and less than one-step behind me. I looked back at her because I had no idea where she wanted me to stop but she took hold of my arm and pressed me on. We finally stopped at cell number 72B and she unlocked the door.

"Git in." she said as she held the door.

I entered the brightly lit standing room only cell. I had to watch were I was stepping as I looked for a vacant spot to plant myself. There must have been fifteen to eighteen girls crowded around the twelve foot by twelve-foot cell. It appeared as if every hooker in the City had been busted that night. Each one of them was just as funky as the others and it sickened me to be associated with them. I wondered if I looked as disheveled as each of them did, just as unkept, funky and abused. I looked around considering each girl, black, white, smelly, dirty. "Do I belong with this group?" Some of them looked as if they might have been "high", but I wasn't sure. Many were dressed in horribly tight tube tops and shorts that left nothing to the imagination. They were so tight on them I wondered how they could possibly be comfortable. Anyone who looked was able see every crease and crack of their bodies including their slit. I heard it called a "camel toe" once, but I wasn't sure how that compared.

They sat and lay on the floor and even the toilet was being used as a chair. Some were sleeping, others talking and laughing and still others looked worried. I had to use the toilet, but it was "right there" in the open for everyone and God to see as I peed. I decided I would rather hold it for now. Maybe Bobby will come and bail me out soon.

I continued to look around, not one of the girl's hair was combed, some looked like they had just come from an all-out, ass kicking, hair pulling, knockdown, drag out bitch fight. Oh, and the makeup they had on would have made Baby Jane cringe.

I could hear someone calling out for their phone call or crying, "I don't belong here." Then I heard a voice asking "Hey, who yo' man?" I turned to see a rather seasoned black ho looking at me with the look a cat might have just before it pounces on some unsuspecting beetle making its way across the kitchen floor.

"I ax you a question ho, who yo' man?" She added to her insistence with bobbing her head from side to side. If it was meant to intimidate, it worked. However, I wasn't about to let her see the intimidation I felt.

"Bobby Roberts" I cocked my head trying to appear tough...and maybe a little black.

"Who he..." another rather gruff looking ho said with a smug egotistical tip of her head so she could look down on me. "He pro'ly some two-bit punk-ass."

One of the other girls behind me reached over and motioned for me to sit by her. I was glad to accommodate; those black hos were rather scary.

"A lot of ho's need to try and pull someone so they don't get a whipping for gettin' busted." She whispered. "Just don't talk to them. They'll leave you be. Try to get some sleep, the time will go by faster."

I told her I had anticipated being bonded out, but she said, "Not at this time of night you won't." She seemed to know what she was talking about.

It was 3:00 am. Court wasn't until 9:00 am.

"That's six hours!" I thought to myself. "Six hours in this smelly cell with all of these funky bitches and I have to PEE!

As the hours went by, I was very amazed that others were able to fall asleep so easily while sitting up against the wall or leaning on each other. I had about two square feet to lie down in. I tried to make my way under the bed slab that jutted out from the concrete wall, but even that didn't have enough room for me to lie down. With five girls on the slab and three under, I gave up any hope of falling asleep.

The entire cell block was extremely noisy with hookers left and right trying to show they were better than the other, or their "man" was "better'n anyone else's man". Now and then, I would hear a girl wailing and another shout "SHUT UP, BITCH" then some more wailing.

"BITCH, YOU BEST SHUT UP!"

In between wails and "SHUT UP'S" another was yelling "MATRON...MAAA...TRON! Who could sleep? I just tried to avoid touching anyone for fear of intruding on their space.

Then all of a sudden, there was a call like a monkey swinging in a cage at a zoo "OO...OO...AH, AH, AH" this strange sound was followed by utter silence as the entire block tried to take in exactly what it was that happened. Then there was another shout.

"Das TARZAN's ladies over dare!" The entire cell block erupted in laughter. I knew who the indignant monkey was, she was Sammy, one of my wife-in-laws. I was used to her outbursts of a caged monkey screeching in frustration. My laughter helped to hide this fact as well as to relieve the tense knots in my gut.

It was about 4:15 am when the matron brought another girl to our cell.

"Good God, don't we have enough in here?" One girl complained.

"Just shut up" the matron's replied as she locked the door again.

The girl came in without hesitation as she made her way to what appeared to be her regular spot and exclaimed "Man, I was beginning to think I wasn't ever gonna get busted." She pushed one of the sleeping girls with her foot. "Move over, bitch."

I admired her fearless confidence among all of the leaches I shared this human cage with. This girl moved into her spot and snuggled right in as if she had just laid down in a comfortable warm bed. I wondered why she was so happy to get busted.

I must have dozed off for a moment or two, because the cell door opening and the announcement that it was time to go, jolted me up. We filed out into the hall single file and led to another larger cell where we were given dry bologna sandwiches, I wolfed mine down. The same ho that was glad to get busted didn't want one. "Those things are nasty," she said. I didn't care, I was starved.

Bobby was in the courtroom and smiled at me as we were all escorted into the front of the courtroom. I had never seen a courtroom before. As I looked around, I saw many people waiting to go up in front of the judge. Some in orange jump suits, others in handcuffs. Some men, some women, but mostly there were ho's sitting all quietly waiting their turn so they could get out and make some money to make up for their lost tricking time.

I overheard the girl next to me telling another girl she hoped to find a trick that would be willing to get a motel room, so she could get some sleep. I interrupted them and asked why she didn't want to go to her apartment.

"I haven't got an apartment." was all she volunteered. I didn't ask her any more questions; I was too stunned.

In the courtroom, there were two well-dressed men at different tables shuffling through papers in briefcases not even looking up until we heard.

"All stand, the honorable Judge Raymond Howard, presiding."

Everyone in the courtroom respectfully stood up as the man wearing what looked like a preacher's robe, quickly walked in and said. "Sit, sit, let's just get through this."

Court was rapid and went the same for each of the hos.

"The charge of loitering. How do you plead?"

"Not guilty"

"Dismissed, insufficient evidence."

He barely looked up from his desk unless the ho took a little too long to answer or she was being charged with soliciting.

When I was called up, my heart leapt in my chest and my knees felt as if they weren't strong enough to hold me as I stood to go up before the judge. There was fear in my gut and my heart beat hard. I had heard all the other ho's cases being dismissed, but that didn't relieve my fear of being convicted and returned to a jail cell.

"Charge?" I heard the judge say.

He wasn't looking at me.

"Loitering." came from the man standing at the table to my left.

I glanced over at the man, he was shuffling papers, seemingly oblivious to my presence. I looked to the judge who now was arranging papers at his desk. A hefty cop stood by the judge's tall desk. His eyes fixed on nothing in particular.

"How do you plead?" I heard the words, but my voice stuck. I looked to the judge who raised his eyes and repeated, "How do you plead?" again, I stood frozen, my words caught in my throat. I felt confused, frightened.

"Is he talking to me? What do I say? I am guilty, but if I say guilty, will I be convicted and sentenced? What should I do?"

I turned to look for an answer to my silent question from Bobby, but he didn't tell me what to say.

"Counsel, advise your client." The impatience was beginning to come through.

The man to my left looked to me then turned to the judge and casually informed the judge that I was pleading "Not guilty"

As I stood there looking at the well-dressed man, I heard the judge make his ruling.

"Insufficient evidence, case dismissed."

"Did he say I could go? Am I okay to leave now? "

"You can leave now."

Without a word, I turned to look at Bobby who was now standing waiting for me. I was free to leave, still in a state of shock, but free to leave the courtroom. Bobby turned to leave and as I followed, I wondered if he was mad that I had been busted. I wondered if I would be beat if I would end up without an apartment and have to be busted so I could sleep.

I was nervous until I saw Bobby was smiling. He asked how I was and if I was hungry.

"Does a bear shit in the woods?" I answered extremely happy that he wasn't mad at me for being thrown into the slammer.

During breakfast, I told Bobby about the girl who was happy to be busted.

"It sounded like she was actually looking for vice to pick her up each night." I explained.

"She may have been." Bobby answered as he took a sip of coffee. "Some hos don't have anywhere to sleep other than jail."

"Really!?" I found it hard to believe that a ho would not be given a place to sleep!

"Yep," he continued as he inspected his steak and eggs the waitress was setting down in front of him. "Some make their girls work until they get busted and then when they get out in the morning, they go back to work."

"Wow, that's horrible."

"Yeah, it is." He continued, "The only way they get to clean themselves up is if they get a trick to rent a room. Then they have to convince the trick to let her keep the key. Sometimes ho's will even trick for the room so they can take a shower and sleep in a bed."

"Wow," I repeated, "that's rough!"

"It's not easy." As he took a bite of his medium rare steak.

It made me think how lucky I was to have an apartment.

Funny to think about it now. I felt lucky. Lucky.

Bobby lowered his head and was silent for a moment. I wondered to myself "He can't be praying, he never does." I didn't ask. A moment later, he looked up at me and said. "There is something I need to tell you."

He went on as I put my fork down and gave my full attention to that "something".

"I've already told the others, but I wanted to tell you." he leaned in close to me and quietly said "You know Martin from the bar on Clark Street?" I knew who he was talking about. Martin was a player, but not in the sense of having any ladies. He did other things was all I knew. He was always happy and while he was a small man, maybe five foot four he couldn't have weighed more than one hundred-twenty pounds. I admired his ability to stay happy even when a fight broke out. Martin would raise his arms out as if he was going to give a big hug to anyone who wanted it, or those who didn't as well. He would raise his arms and smile while he would say something like "Now, guys, guys, we're having a good time here, why you want me to get ol' Bubba to throw you out in the street for? I don't wan dat, I don't like Bubba." then Martin would whisper something about being afraid that Bubba was a bit of a fag and that he liked to try and kiss him after throwing people out. Martin would talk as if Bubba was always after him and how he gave him the heebie-jeebies. Then the fight would break up and go back to being fun.

"Martin was killed last night."

I was stunned. I didn't know what to say, Martin was great, and he got along with everyone including Bubba who really wasn't gay. Martin just used that because of how large of a man he was.

Bobby explained "He was at the bar last night and in the middle of a big party, someone went behind the bar apparently to give Martin a hug,

but he stuck him with a knife in the middle of the hug. The guy then turned around laughing with the crowd as if nothing happened."

"Wow" was all I could say.

"Martin was holding his gut, but everyone just thought he was playing until he fell, and they saw the blood."

I asked if they got the guy, but Bobby said no one knew who he was, and he snuck out before anyone noticed he was gone.

I wanted to go to his funeral however, I also knew that would be impossible because anyone who knew Martin and showed their self would be questioned. This would draw too much attention on us, so, no, to attend this man's funeral was impossible.

I thought about Martin now and then, quietly grieving for the man. There would be no mention of an arrest or even a murder investigation, ever, and the man's name would never be mentioned even in passing. We would never go back to the bar either, it was as if it no longer existed. I wondered why we couldn't go back. I wanted to see the last spot Martin drew a breath. Bobby said no. I found this very confusing.

Bobby put us back in the hotel with George the bellman bringing tricks up for us. The streets again, were hot with the election coming up and the murder investigation going on.

"Right now, we do not have a choice." Bobby told us "You will be safer in the hotel. I'll be back in the mornings to take everyone to breakfast."

And that was that. George took us up to our rooms and let us in. I sat on the bed and turned the television on.

"Wonder woman" It's a Wonder she is still on television." I changed the channel.

"MASH" I really don't like that show," I thought to myself, "Love the music...hate the show, it's a war time sitcom, it'll never last."

I left the dial on MASH while I listened to the music. Somewhere I had heard that the theme music was a song titled "Suicide is Painless" I wondered if it really was. I decided to keep the program on, my only other choice was "Starsky and Hutch".

The hotel was nice in that I didn't have to take a chance of being busted. George would only let people he knew not to be cops in. For that guarantee, George earned forty percent of what each girl made and all the tips he could get from the trick. He probably made more than we did in one night.

I had planned on getting a book of names and phone numbers along with how much they spent. I was going to surprise Bobby with this trick book and see if I could get him to allow us to work out of an apartment rather than a hotel.

My next trick asked if he could call me outside of the hotel.

"I don't like coming to this place and I like you!" he explained.

"I'm really not supposed to give out my phone number...but, there is nothing that says I can't take your number." it was the first number in my little book of tricks.

The money might be better, since they will be coming to an apartment rather than picking up "God knows what" off of the street, or paying for a hotel room, tipping the bellman and then paying for ten to fifteen minutes of fun.

Marla was a relatively new girl that Bobby had pulled. She seemed nice, not someone who would stab you in the back. When I had been collecting the numbers, likes, dislikes and how much they spent for a couple of weeks, I was so excited I was busting at the seams to tell someone.

Just then Marla knocked on my door.

"Bobby wants us to meet him in DeeDee's room to go to breakfast." She said.

I pulled her in my room and said, "I have to tell someone..."

After telling Marla all about my secret trick book, my excitement seemed to be a bit contagious and Marla was grinning from ear to ear.

She asked how many names I had collected.

"Well," I began "I haven't been taking everyone's number, just the ones that spend twenty-five or more, and only if I like them." Marla knew what I meant when I said "liked them" because I had told her before I got nothing out of the sex. When I said, "liked them", I was referring to their personality and what I picked up from our short time together.

"I suppose I have about ten or fifteen names." I continued, "But I want a whole book of tricks before I show him."

At breakfast that morning, Marla knew I had brought the notebook with me so no one would find it in the room while I was gone. She also knew how excited I was about the book.

"Kim, why don't you show Bobby your surprise?" She said unexpectedly.

"Crap"

"Surprise? surprise?" Bobby quizzically looked across the table at me

"Uh," I stammered "I wasn't ready to show you yet."

With that, Bobby's temper began to flare. I could see it in his eyes. He would get a look that was similar to that of a panther gives when she feels threatened. His look was very threatening. He did not like his girls keeping secrets.

Marla broke in again "Go ahead, Kim" I glanced in her direction "Show him, I know you have it in your bag." I was wondering why she would do such a thing after I swore her to secrecy and that could put me in danger of being beat if I didn't show him.

I looked back at Bobby and noticed that DeeDee was looking at me with a devilish look in her eyes. She was curious, but then again, she hoped it would earn me a whipping.

"You best tell me now, girl" Bobby warned.

I knew that voice, it was Bobby's last nerve speaking. I bit my lips nervously as I reached into my bag. I was sure he was going to grab the bag right out of my hand, but he didn't.

I handed him the ruffled notebook and tried to explain.

"I've been collecting names"

"Here it comes," I thought, "If I only had more names the idea of a whore-house might intrigue him enough that breaching the rule of not turning any of the hotels tricks outside of the hotel walls would be forgiven."

I continued "I thought if I got enough names we could work out of an apartment and keep all of the money rather than giving the bellman a cut." Bobby became noticeably quiet.

I could see him scrutinizing each note I made including whether they asked me for a number, or if I asked them. I continued holding my gaze as I nervously waited for Bobby's reaction. Marla seemed excited almost giddy, while DeeDee seemed more curious than vengeful at this point.

After a few minutes of nail-biting nervousness, Bobby looked up. I had hoped I would see a smile, but he still looked a bit angry.

"Will any of these tricks tell George?" he quizzed.

"No, they all said they didn't want George to know." I insisted, knowing my answer could determine my fate.

"Are you SURE!" he barked.

I jumped as if he raised his arm to hit me right there in the restaurant. Fearfully I answered him. "YES, I'm SURE!"

Bobby took a look at the book again as the waitress put our plates down in front of us. Bobby sat back so she could put his food down, too. He never looked up at her when she asked if we needed anything. A moment later, he put the book down and looked around the table.

"This is good," he finally announced with just a bit of surprise in his voice. A sigh of relief silently escaped my lips. I felt my entire body relax. I hadn't even realized that I had tensed every muscle in my body until that moment. I took a deep breath and again, allowed it to escape through the slight opening between my lips.

We were all instructed to collect names and numbers and warned to be cautious in our quest for the next "Ho's guide to an easier life - the little black trick book"

Chapter 11

The new apartment we were to move into was small and the entire building smelled like yesterday's Mexican food. Even in the late evenings or middle of the night, the odor of left-over taco meat and refried beans that had been left out all night, filled the air. It was a furnished studio apartment, which meant the furnishings were infused with the odors.

We were on the fifth floor, which meant a creaking, squeaking, slow ride up the old elevator I swore was getting ready to snap a rusted cable and plummet down the shaft killing us all. The hallways were long, dark and filthy. I doubt the carpets had been vacuumed in years, if ever. In fact, we joked about being from the Black Foot Indian tribe because our feet were constantly blackened from the carpets and the years of built up dust, dirt, and spills of "God knows what."

One short trip to the trash shoot inducted you into the Black Foot tribe. For a while, we decided to go barefoot, but found that dark socks or just wearing shoes was probably the best way to keep our feet clean... but it wasn't guaranteed.

Inside the apartment, I noticed the darkness, even on that sunny day darkness took over like the ominous dark cloud that looms over a neighborhood just before the wind ushers in the storm. It carried with it a heavy load of depression that only denial or God, if you allowed Him, could lighten. The single 1950's overhead lamp made little difference in brightening up the place. The only window looked out over a chain link fenced area and beyond that were only more dark buildings.

The living room was fair sized and there was a separate kitchen with a small four-burner stove and an oven that was about half the size of a normal oven. The sink was small as was the refrigerator. I opened the door on the fridge and found the small freezer's, familiar baby blue door. There was no seal on the door to keep it closed tight, in fact I wondered why it had a separate door at all because it remained slightly ajar even with the refrigerator door closed. If it wasn't defrosted regularly, you might have to invest in a small jackhammer to get the hamburger for dinner out from all the ice. Cautiously, I opened the flimsy blue freezer door. I was afraid of what I may find leering out. I strongly suspected it had not been defrosted for an awfully long time. I was right.

"We aren't going to be able to buy ice cream any time soon." I whispered to myself in disgust. I knew if it was going to be defrosted, I would be the one who would have to do it.

The small metal table included two metal chairs with the iconic dirty yellow vinyl seat that sported one crack positioned just right to pinch a thigh as you sat down. A short hallway, if you could call it that, led to a small green bathroom. It was just then I realized I hadn't seen any bedroom! There was a separate kitchen, a five-foot hall and a bathroom, but no bedroom.

"Where's the bedroom?" I asked in surprise.

"Oh," Bobby said with a wink towards DeeDee. "It's in the closet."

I looked at both Bobby and DeeDee in disbelief. "How could there be a bedroom in a closet? How could you even get a bed in a closet?"

Bobby's smile began to grow as he told me "Go, take a look."

"It's in there." He assured, "Take a look if you don't believe me."

I hesitated but he took my hand and led me over to the closet door. "Go ahead"

It looked like a regular door, not any wider than a normal closet door, either. I wasn't sure if I should believe him or not. Then, Bobby slowly opened the door and…sure enough, there was a bed in the closet...standing upright against the wall that backed up to the living room.

"Huh?" I said in disbelief. I had never seen such a thing. I wondered how we would ever be able to get it out of there each night and then if we were expected to get it back into the closet before we went to work each day...I just didn't understand the reasoning of this "bed in a closet".

"Who puts a bed in a closet?"

Bobby laughed as he saw the confused look in my eyes and explained "It's a Murphy bed."

"What's a Murphy bed?" I asked even more confused than ever.

"It's a bed that folds down at night and during the day can be put back up." I was trying to grasp the idea, but it just wasn't coming.

The mattress was against the right-side wall of the closet, how could this thing possibly work?

"Beds just don't fold!" I reasoned.

I followed DeeDee and Bobby into the living room where a set of French style doors I had not noticed before were. Bobby opened each door in turn as if he was a white gloved butler preparing the master bedroom for the night.

"Whaaat?" I said as I looked at the top of a bed with a metal footboard folded flat against the mattress and at the floor level, the headboard folded up to the mattress.

Most likely with my mouth open, I thought to myself, "How in the world can you sleep on such a thing."

Bobby and DeeDee laughed as I took a cautious step back in case the bed decided to fall.

Casually, Bobby strolled to the far side of the bed and in full butler mode, pulled with only one hand. It twisted around just like one of those fancy hotel revolving doors! I saw the legs of the double sized bed were folded flat against the under springs and wondered how this would take shape. He continued his silent demonstration by taking a hold of the metal frame and gently pulling it down toward the floor. I could hear the stretching of the metal springs that held the bed in place. Then, to my surprise, the whole thing unfolded and systematically took on the shape of a full-sized bed thereby converting the living room into the master bedroom.

"WHOA" I said, "a full-sized bed that folds out of a closet! What will they think of next?" Bobby and DeeDee looked at each other and laughed as I stood there in awe of this fantastically simple technological use of space!

The apartment was situated right in the middle of "HO's-row," just a couple of blocks from our apartment was Old town. It was where the out-of-towners went to see the famed "Ripley's Believe It Or Not museum" and take a picture with "Double-eyed Loo Min" or " wax statue of a "Sky clad witch" and shrunken heads, take in a live show at Faces or eat at any number of bars and restaurants that lined the famous street. Then, if it was so desired it was where those looking for some company would go to find a "date". That is until the cops got wind of the hot spot and patrolled the short stro sending ho's and tricks to other parts of the city.

Now and then, if I was bored, I'd go down there to look around. I didn't go very often because if I was spotted, I'd get in trouble. I spent more time looking over my shoulder than checking out the sights of Wells Street.

The apartment on Dearborn Street may have been an excellent location and convenient for our needs, but for me, it was at a time of depression and fear. Working the streets wasn't easy. Vice was an ever-present threat and periodically we would be told to run from doorway to doorway to avoid being arrested. If the vice situation got too hot, such as around election time, Bobby would take us off of the street and put us to working a bar or a hotel like the Mark Twain, where I stayed at when I first came to Chicago. The change helped at times, it felt like a time that held little if not any stress on making enough money in one night. If we didn't earn very much, it wasn't because of something we did or didn't do, it was because the bellman didn't bring us enough.

There was one sad thing about working in a hotel, no apartment. Bobby felt there was no reason to keep an apartment when we could just as easily sleep at the hotel. He would never say anything, it was just no longer available.

"When we get a day off, can we go to the apartment?"

"What the hell do you need an apartment for?!" He would bark. "What's wrong with sleeping at the hotel?" That was when we knew he got rid of it.

"Our tricks come here because they can trust the girls won't steal and that they don't have any kind of disease." Bellman George said. "And, if I bring a trick up and you're asleep, you'll get no more tricks that night."

"If you fall asleep," Bobby warned, "You and I will have a problem."

I knew exactly what that meant, and so did the others.

Even though the hotels were dirty, smelly, cockroach infested, no air conditioning, sheets that may or may not have been changed in a while and toilet paper so hard I actually wrote a letter on it and mailed it, I still preferred to work out of them. I didn't have to look for the tricks and I didn't have to worry if I picked up a cop or a trick with the clap or syphilis. The bellmen would only allow those he knew because of the trouble he and the hotel would face. He only allowed girls he knew not to have bad reputations to work out of the rooms, so it was imperative we minded our P's and Q's if we didn't want back on the streets.

However, there were those nights that would be horribly slow and at one o'clock in the morning, television signed off thereby, making it incredibly difficult to stay awake. Many times, I would be found asleep and pay for it with no work the rest of the night and them pay a second time with Bobby the next day.

Each night as the broadcasting day signed off, fear crept in. A fear that comes from living in a buried jar of Kimchi for the last five years and you come out to find Antonio Banderas standing right in front of you. You look at him with the sudden realization that you are covered in fermented cabbage and fish heads. But it doesn't matter. He takes you in his strong arms and leans you back as he whispers "mi amor, mi vida, mi belleza" then looking Deep into your eyes he passionately kisses...

"What in the Hell are you talking about woman!" my husband said contorting his face in my direction. He had been listening, I guess I couldn't get away with even a little embellishment. He continued, "Antonio Banderas was fifteen years old back then. He grew up in Spain!"

"Ok, ok, I know, he wasn't in Chicago in 1975." I thought about it for a moment. But he is like... DAMN... Know what I mean?

Watching the familiar image of a flag while America, the Beautiful plays on the television I dreaded the short test pattern that would come next and then the station would go off. At the end of the song, a voice announces the end of the broadcasting day. I held on to each sound and each image prior to the stations sign off. I held on to it because it meant I had nothing to keep my mind occupied and awake. Then for only a quick second the black and white bullseye comes on before that all too familiar and depressing fuzzy static sound. Typically, I had a rough time staying awake and when I felt myself droop, my heart would take a sudden leap. I realized that even though I was watching the signing off, I did not remember the end of the movie I had been watching. Most of the movies were typically boring and a real chore to get through. I didn't have much of a choice with the other two channels, CBS and ABC signing off an hour earlier.

"Had I fallen asleep? I have to stay awake!" I told myself. I shook my head every time I felt myself fading back to my dreamless sleep, but it didn't help very much.

That fear of missing a trick and the bellman reporting to Bobby kept slapping me in the face.

"WAKE UP! WAKE UP!" I yelled silently to myself. "STAY...STay...AWAKE! AWake... I'll just rest my eyes for a few seconds...... "

Then, just that quick, I heard his words before I saw him standing in front of me. He was counting out some money into my upturned hand while saying "Very good, very good"

I watched as he passed by me heading for the door, I stood in complete bewilderment as he happily closed the door behind him. I held my confused gaze for a few more moments. I looked down at my hand, yes, the twenty dollars was still there.

"Did I fall asleep and the bellman brought me a trick?"

"Did I drag him in from the hallway?"

I looked around the room as if somehow the answer to my question would be revealed. "Was I so afraid of getting beat for falling asleep that I actually turned a trick in MY SLEEP???"

These questions rolled around and around "What should I do?"

"Should I call the bellman and tell him how much he spent? But if I dragged the trick in from the hall, what would the bellman say when I told him I got twenty dollars. Would he tell Bobby I got some poor unsuspecting trick to come into my room for a second go round with me?"

I looked at the clock, 3:38 am.

More questions, "How long had I been with him, ten minutes? An hour? A couple of hours???" again, I asked "What should I do?"

I had stalled long enough, I had to do something. I warily walked over to the phone and dialed "0" still questioning, still wondering what to say or should I ask, "No, he'll think I'm an idiot and tell Bobby." As I stood there, naked and clutching the twenty dollars. A familiar gravelly voice on the other end answered "George."

He sounded his usual dry self.

"Uh," I hesitated, "He spent twenty."

"Okay" was his reply as he hung up.

I sat down on the ruffled bed, still clutching the bills, still trying to make sense of the strange event and vowing to never let it happen again and to never tell anyone, especially Bobby.

I couldn't believe I actually turned a trick while I was sound asleep. I was so scared that I would get beat if Bobby found out. I decided something had to change. I asked Bobby if I could go back out on the street. Everyone thought I had lost my mind. Hotel work was a cakewalk compared to walking the streets, but I didn't want to take a chance.

"It's too hot on the streets right now" Bobby said.

Bobby was referring to the heat that the cops put on the ho's and pimps during election time. It was what the politicians would do to help their self to be elected. Once the election was over, everything would go back to normal and we could come out of hiding.

"You'll have to stay here for a little while. Once it cools off you can go back out on the streets if you still want to."

"Okay" I couldn't argue with him, but I wondered if tricking in a hotel was truly safer or not. After all, out on the streets, I wouldn't have to worry about falling asleep.

Chapter 12

You could say that working a hotel was easy, however, for every yin there is a yang. For every smile of approval, there is the backhand of blame and for every act of compassion, comes retaliation of equal or greater impact.

I opened the door to find two men, obviously the bellman and my next trick. He was Indian, not so much in his appearance, but he had a very thick accent with limited English.

"THIS IS KIM!" George yelled, apparently believing that if you don't know English, you are also deaf.

"Hi," I stepped aside for him to come in.

It was my first trick I was to turn while on my period. I wasn't too happy about it, and worried about bleeding through. However, when I told Bobby, I was shocked to learn that it didn't matter.

"Well you can still turn tricks."

"What do I do, then?" I asked

He told DeeDee to get me a sponge. With a silent snarl, she went to the bathroom, retrieving a small natural sponge she took aim and threw it across the room at me. I felt she was being crass, but Bobby didn't seem to think anything about it.

I turned the strange golf ball sized sponge over and over in my hand as I wondered how I was to use it. "What, I mean, how, um, what do I do?" I was very confused.

"DeeDee, tell her how to use it." Bobby said as he left us alone.

DeeDee wasn't too pleased to explain this, she still felt invaded on by me. "Just shove it up." She couldn't be anymore snippy.

I asked how to get it out since there didn't seem to be any apparent means of retrieving it. "You reach up and get it out!"

Wow, that's disgusting. I had never even considered such a disgusting act. I knew I had to do it, but I worried about losing it up there. YUCK!

Excusing myself, I motioned to my new friend that I would be in the bathroom. I sat there looking at this thing, again, turning it over in my hand, squishing the warm water-soaked lump between my fingers. I hesitated even proceeding with this masquerade when I thought, okay, honesty is the best policy. So, with conviction and a little hesitation, I shoved the sponge up inside of me and went out to inform the man I was to have sex with the whole sponge thing.

I explained my predicament, as well as, the solution to which this man about had a heart attack. His panic was increasing as he stepped away from me. He was holding his arms up in a defensive manner as he spit out words in English and a language I could not determine.

I stepped towards him as he stepped away. He seemed afraid to get close to me.

"No, no, no...you...dirty" was all I could understand. His fear appeared genuine and it seemed to be a fear linked to his religion, however, I wasn't sure.

"Money, back, please, money back." He was able to let me know this without question.

I knew I wasn't supposed to give his money back, it was something I had been told when I first started.

"And, once you have his money in your hands, never, ever give it back." Bobby told me this in no uncertain terms. It didn't seem right, but it was one of his cardinal rules. "No returns, no refunds."
"Okay" was all I could say.

I felt sympathetic towards the trick as well as realizing that I was risking an unleashing of Bobby's anger, but I really felt it was the right thing to do. Being on my period was something very traumatic to him and it wasn't as if he knew this before he gave me his twenty-five dollars. Surely Bobby would understand and agree with me.

"You gave him the money BACK?!" His face began to show his anger. His body became rigid and his eyes locked on only me. I saw the other girls cautiously stepping back leaving me to receive the full brunt of his wrath.

I didn't even see it coming. The back of his hand landed hard on the side of my head knocking me off balance and sending me into the dresser beside me. My ribs landed square on the edge, but I only felt it for a second. As I regained my footing another blow caught me on the other side sending me over to the bed.

"Never, EVER, give the money back!" he yelled. "WHAT do you think you were doing, girl?! " Grabbing my arm and pulling me up, the look in his eyes reiterated the words: "YOU better hope George doesn't kick you out...along with the rest of us!" Shoving me down on the bed he shouted "NEVER...EVER fuck with a man's money!" Those in the room stepped aside providing a path for Bobby to leave. His fists still clinched, shoulders tensed and squared off.

When Bobby reached the elevator and signaled the bellman to take him down, he didn't look back and no one moved or closed the door to my room until the elevator door closed and the rumble of wheels, cables and two angry men made its way down.

Later, while alone, I thought through the entire evening of events. Still I felt the man deserved his money back and while I never regretted my actions, I decided I would never let myself get in that position again. However, if I did, it would be easier to give it back on the streets.

There were three new girls added to Bobby's stable, Heidi, Brenda and Maria. Maria was a beautiful Hispanic girl, tall and slender with long, thick, wavy black hair. We hit it off very well and became close friends very quickly. I felt safe with her and when I was around her, I didn't feel so alone. Still, I was too afraid to confide in her my deepest desires or darkest fears concerning Bobby.

Brenda, Big-Boobed wanna-be Brenda as we referred to her, joined us about the same time as Heidi. Brenda was a runaway from a sexually abusive father.

I didn't know Heidi's story other than Bobby had bought her from another pimp who was looking to get rid of her...similar to what Bobby did with Carmen.

Carmen...I hadn't thought about her in a long time. She worshiped Satan, it was the only thing I couldn't tolerate about her. I was a Christian, she worshiped Satan. We were the best of friends, but I would not set foot in her mom's apartment because of the alter she had.

Bobby had sold her to someone who eventually gave her some money to take a bus back home. I was envious of her because of that. Bobby wanted to get rid of her because she and I were friends and he didn't like friends that were too close.

I learned later that someone had killed her shortly after she settled back home. It was ruled a suicide even though she was only five foot, one and the weapon used to murder her was a double-barreled shot gun found on the other side of the room. Carmen...committing suicide...she was always smiling and excited about something...it was very difficult for me to accept.

Heidi was a very tall girl with short blond hair. She was a happy go lucky girl, with one aim in this life, to get a boob job. She was almost completely flat chested, and it wouldn't have surprised me to find out that her sole reason for getting into this life was to get someone, anyone, to pay for breast implants. I suspect that Bobby knew that was all she wanted from him and if he ever gave her the money for it, she would leave as quick as lightening.

Heidi quite often seem very proud of being a prostitute. It was almost a badge of honor to her. As a matter of fact, Heidi loved the attention she got so much, it didn't bother her to get busted or let anyone to know she was a ho.

"Hey, Kim, I got the crabs from some trick. How do I get rid of them?" She asked

"Well," I began, "I think there's a shampoo that you can get from the drug store." I had never had them, myself, but I overheard DeeDee talking about the stuff with Bobby.

Heidi asked if I wanted to go to the corner drug store and help her find the right stuff. It seemed like the right thing to do, so I agreed to go along.

I liked going to drug stores, they always had the coolest things to look at. They had of course, greeting cards and beautiful little figurines, shiny crystal angels with gold tipped wings and beautiful angelic faces. Sometimes there were unicorns with spiral horns and tiny bits of gold flecks intertwined with the swirled glass of the horn to reflect an ever so faint indication that this mythical creature of ordinary glass might hold the magical power that could whisk you off to a time long ago when life was easy and happy. To be touched gently by the tip of her horn would be heavenly and most welcomed. The crystal unicorns were very fragile with the fair tail draping down and the dainty legs made by drawing liquid glass from the chest down into delicate hooves prancing. I worried about touching one for fear of breaking one of those legs. Still, I couldn't help to gently touch the mythical creature and cradle it in both hands, turning it over and over as I examined each intricate piece before carefully replacing it to its original home on the glass shelf then reaching for the equally delicate angel that stood humbly and lovingly beside the unicorn. On the next display you could fine the novelty items like pet-rocks, which I found idiotic.

When someone would say they wanted a pet rock, I would tell her to go outside and adopt some gravel. You can also find Chia pets, guaranteed to grow, or double your money back. Mine never grew. I never tried to get my money back. Too much of an advantage.

One of the greatest things that drug stores had were soda fountains. Usually identified by the long white countertop along one side or the other with stools bolted to the floor that would twist completely around. Behind the counter was the person who would create some of the most wonderful sprinkle topped sundaes you had ever tasted. The smell and sound of the frying hamburgers and French fries bubbling in the hot vat of grease permeated the store enticing the customers to treat themselves "just this once".

There were cosmetics, bath salts, hand lotion and exfoliating products for whatever exfoliating products do.

Drug stores always had a lot more to look at than simply remedies for every ailment known to man.

"Cool, let's go," Heidi said.

It was a hot afternoon, and the soda fountain was almost completely filled with patrons looking for a cool treat to enjoy and the check register was working overtime with others paying for items they didn't need so they could catch just a few minutes of heaven in the highly coveted air-conditioning . They were so busy that by the time we were ready to checkout, there was a long line stretching back past the bandages and ointments behind the tanning lotion and along the unicorns and angels. Eventually, when there were just a few patrons in front of us all relatively calm minding their own business Heidi asked,

"How long does this take to work, these things are drivin' me nuts?"

She looked a bit uncomfortable. "I don't know, read the instructions."

As Heidi was trying to read the tiny print, I noticed an older woman behind us holding some Noxzema, Pepsodent tooth powder, and a box of tissue. She was looking straight at us with the strangest stare I had ever seen.

I was beginning to feel extremely conspicuous. I just knew she was looking at us thinking we were terrible people who have "sex with complete strangers for money". She must be judging us to be disgusting young girls who should be ashamed of ourselves. I couldn't hide from this woman's unpleasant profiling and shock of seeing, not one, but two hussies up so close.

"She's staring at us." I whispered to Heidi, trying to be as discrete as possible.

Heidi raised her eyes from the box and looked around at all the people.

"Where?"

"Behind you with the box of tissue." I answered.

Heidi was now staring at the woman who had now turned her attention to the small box clearly marked "Lice Shampoo."

With a smile and a quick little lift of the bottled exterminator, Heidi proudly told the lady

"Occupational hazard."

Chapter 13

"Yawl get dressed, I want to take you somewhere."

Secretly I hoped we were going out to party. It had been a long and difficult day and I desperately wanted to quit for the night. Bobby, as usual, didn't explain anything and I knew better than to ask. We were to follow his lead and do exactly as we were told. Don't ask, and above all… don't think. I know this because every time I said, "I just thought…" he would snap back at me with "WELL, DON'T THINK!"

"Okay."

No one said a word until we arrived. We parked right along State Street in the front of a bar. It was the type of bar that didn't want to attract any attention. Flat red brick outside, two small rectangular windows set too high to look inside to see what was happening, it wouldn't matter anyway, because it was too dark inside to see much of anything until your eyes adjusted to the dim lighting. The corner entrance was just as unassuming with a door that was similar to the back door of the old greasy-spoon café down the street. It resembled a back-alley exit used by a hefty, cigar smoking, cook who hasn't shaved for two days. The door that was used to throw out any food left on the patron's plates once they left the restaurant.

Walking through the corner doorway, we could see that the only light in the place was a faint glow of the stage lights that illuminated the tiny stage behind an "L" shaped bar. The stage, which couldn't have been any bigger than Tom Thumb's guest room, held nothing interesting than a small, very worn, spindle chair sitting patiently next to a red curtain, which the dancers came through when it was her turn to dance. I considered this lowly chair's purpose, was it waiting for a tired dancer or possibly it was left by a maintenance worker who stood on the chair to reach a burnt-out light bulb? My ignorance in the area of striptease dancing was amazing. The floor of the stage was tiled and reminded me of the worn-out tile in our apartment's kitchen.

The music that was playing was loud and came from a jukebox with such titles as "Lady Marmalade Moulin Rouge" bewitching the listener with, "Voulez-vous coucher avec moi, ce soir?" and a favorite for ho's on all corners everywhere, "Diamond in the Back" sung by Curtis Mayfield.

"But remember brothers and sisters
You can still stand tall
Just be thankful, for what you've got
Diamond in the back, sunroof top,
Diggin' the scene with a gangsta lean oo, oo, oo"

The best part of the song was, of course "Diamond in the back, sunroof top, diggin' the scene with a gangsta lean" which every lady silently relished in the imagery of that verse.

No one was paying any real attention to the person moving slow to the music in a rather suggestive way up on the stage, we just followed Bobby between the small dark tables and the row of sparsely occupied bar stools. It was obvious this was not a player's bar and when Bobby takes us to a new bar, we never sit at the tables he simply tells us to "go to work". So, when we sat at a table we were all a little unsure of what to do and a little curious of what to expect.

We ordered our drinks and were surprised when Bobby and the bartender served us. Bobby seemed to be somewhat familiar with this man and introduced us one at a time.

Whitey, the bartender, stood cross-armed with an uninterested gaze listening to Bobby. I could see that Bobby was more interested than this faceless man. It was almost as if he was just humoring Bobby as he met us. Although he didn't appear interested, he also appeared stern as he used his height to establish seniority and dominance. There was also a small wisp of professional attitude as demonstrated by the way he dressed and his short-cropped white hair combed over to one side, hence the nickname, Whitey.

Whitey was stocky, seasoned and unequivocally the most non-committing person I have ever seen. I'm sure I wasn't the only one trying to figure this guy out,

I don't think the man has any facial muscles. The entire time we were there, I never saw so much as a twinkle in his eye, vague grin, or even down turned eyebrows.

"… this is Kim, Sammy, Marie, and DeeDee." Whitey stood looking straight ahead as if he was being introduced to a piece of tree bark. Still trying to size this man up I thought "could be a trick." but he didn't seem the type. But…whoever he is, it didn't matter because it was obvious that he was important to Bobby which meant…he was important to us.

Bobby and Whitey stepped away from the table to talk without the addition of four sets of ears pretending not to be listening in. After a few quick minutes, Whitey turned and walk back to tending bar, refilling drinks and cleaning the counter.

Bobby returned to the table and said, "Let's go."

No one asked any questions, but I was dying to know what just happened as I am sure the other girls were.

A few days later while I was walking the stro' Bob pulled up. "Kim, Get in." Dutifully, I did as I was told wondering what was up. It was commonplace to see Bob, now and then, driving past but for him to stop one of us from making him some money was unusual.

"You got anything going?" Interesting question since he just saw me by myself on the street, if I had caught a trick, I could not be seen with him. Typically, I would lead him to a motel or the apartment. It helped to keep both of us safe and there was no one walking behind me.

"Nothing right now," I answered "But I have done a little. I've got about forty-five."

I wasn't sure how much I had all together because I never really kept track of the money or tricks for that matter. Why bother, it all went to him anyway. The only time I kept track was when Bobby would try to put a quota on us. He would do this whenever he watched a movie about hookers or heard about other pimps having quotas with their ladies. For some reason he would get the hair-brained idea that he was just too nice to us and needed to assert his pimp-hood now and then. It always put the "Fear of Bob" into us and he reveled in this, it turned him on. If one of us did not make the quota, he would become incredibly angry. He soon found out that it was not worth it. We actually made less money! Either someone did not make the quota, or they thought it was quitting time if reached it.

"I get to go home now, right? I made the quota."

"Girl, how'd you make that so fast." Bob would ask.

"I had this one trick who asked me what I needed to get to go home. When I told him," she smiled, *"he gave it to me!"*

This went over like a ground squirrel trying to fly on the tail of an eagle.

"Girl, get back out there and make some more money."

He would eventually give up on the idea until another hooker movie came on. We learned very fast to not let him see when this kind of movie was on.

When Bob took me to Whiteys, I was a little surprised Bob did not gather up the other girls. Maybe they weren't available, maybe they all were with tricks, or maybe Bob had some other idea in his head.

As we sat down at the end of the bar, Bob leaned close to me and whispered. "Don't look, but the dancers on the stage…" He whispered as he held his hand up by his mouth pretending he was just resting his head on the back side of his hand. The dancers up there… " I looked intently at Bob as he continued "…are really guys."

My mouth dropped into my lap, my eyes jumped out of my head and shot right up to the stage. "Hey, Hey, Hey." Bobby said pulling my arm bringing my attention back to him. "I told you not to look."

"Oh crap, he did" I tried very hard to keep my gaze where it was supposed to be, but it was harder than I would have ever thought. My eyes migrated to the stage where these women were dancing around spinning pasties around showing off their talent of spinning one, one way and the other one the other way.

I grappled for my words, "They are guys?! But, they got boobs and I don't see their dicks!"

Bob snickered and explained to me that they were "drag queens".

"They have breast implants and they tape their dicks back so it's not visible."

"No" I insisted. "Really?" It was beyond my comprehension. A man who pushes his balls up into his pelvic area and tapes his dick back between his legs to make it appear as if he is a woman. Wow, that is wild.

"Some of them are waiting for an operation to make them into women." My mind reeled at the idea. These dancers are boys dressed like girls, dancing in flowing sheer wraps and G-strings with absolutely no sign of a dick or balls

"You can tell they're guys because they have Adam's apples and their wrists are larger than most women's." Bob continued as I tried not to stare, but I kept finding my eyes slowly moving back onto the dancers with Bob pulling my attention back to where it belonged.

"KIM" he whispered angrily, "don't stare!" drawing me back to him.

"So, are they called he's or she's?" I asked.

"They like to be called she."

"Craaaapp" was all I could think of to say.

As we finished our drinks, Whitey came over and in his warmed-over disposition said, "So, she'll be here tomorrow?" His eyes never left Bobby other than to wipe his hands on the bar towel he carried everywhere.

I wondered why Whitey would not look in my direction at all, later I learned that it was out of respect to Bobby. I belonged to Bobby and Whitey looking at me for any other reason than by Bobby's invitation would be seen as a sign of disrespect.

I belonged...I belonged...Never in my life had I ever thought of myself as a thing that belonged to someone before....

Whitey was very particular about who could work his bar. He would not let just any ho walk in off the street and Whitey was only accepting me out of Bobby's girls. He felt they were not up to his caliber. When Bob tried to tell him that we were a package deal, Whitey put Bob in his place and laid it all out.

"Look here, this is my bar and I call the shots. When the girls are here, they work for me, understand? Not you, me! And if you or your girls try to tell me how to run this business, you're out of here and your girls will never work here, Got IT? AND...if you don't like it, take your girls somewhere else."

Bob begrudgingly agreed, submitting to Whitey's authority within his bar. This thoroughly shocked me. -Bob Roberts bowing down to a barkeep.

Whitey ran his bar very professional, he guaranteed the girls that the tricks were good and were not dangerous or perverts. "If they give you any problem or try and cheat you, tell me and they will never come here again." That made me smile but then he laid out his laws. "If you work here, you work here, got it? You don't turn any tricks outside of this place, if you do, you're out. If a cop comes in, I'll let you know and ALL tricking stops. If you get busted, I get busted and I am not about to go sit in any jail cell." Then he said HIS girls were clean.

HIS GIRLS, he actually claimed ownership of every ho in his bar!

"If any girl gives any trick the clap she's out. Got it?"
"And no drug addicts!" Whitey's rules were very explicit, no if's, and's, or but's about it. "If you come in high, you're out."
He should have called this place "Whitey's - You're Out"
"I know every cop in the district" Whitey continued, "and I'll let you know when one comes in. All tricking stops until I tell you." He insisted. "I'm not going to be put out of business because you decide you can do what you want."
"You steal from a trick, you're out. You don't do as I say, you're out."
No that, or you're out, got it, no this or you're out, he's out... the rules at whitey's went on and on, I found myself worried I would break one without realizing it then I'd be out.
"All my tricks know if they come in here with the clap, they're out for ever. I will let you know if a trick is interested in you. How much you get is up to you, but you will not trick out of here for less than twenty-five, got it? You turn a trick for less, you're out! And don't think about cheating me because, if I catch you and I will catch you, you're out." For this, Whitey received 40% of every dime passed from trick to ho and it was to be paid immediately upon return. Whitey would not repeat any of his laws, but he would let Bob know if they were broken and I knew what that would mean for me.

Whitey would not let me start right away, I actually had to wait until the next night. I didn't understand why, it was just a policy he had.

Bob told me that I had to do really good in this bar so Whitey would take a chance with the others.

"At least DeeDee, anyway."

That next day the time Whitey said, Bob walked me into the bar.

"Sit over there, I'll be back." Bobby told me.

Interestingly, I found myself a bit nervous. It felt like I was on trial. Not the court kind of trial, like you might think, but a trial to see if I was worthy.

I had just been hit and humiliated in front of the other girls for doing what was right. I gave the money back to a trick whose religion said a woman was "unclean" if she was on her period. He was very much afraid and put in the position again, I would do the same thing.

Since George, the bellman was angry, he hadn't planned to send any more tricks to my room that night.

"BITCH!" I heard as the door opened again. "Get your things! George isn't bringing any more tricks to you, so I got to find somewhere else." Bob started throwing things at me to hurry me up. He already got the other girls from their rooms, they were quietly waiting by the elevator as instructed by Bob.

I could see the anger in Bob's brisk walk, arms at his side. I was glad to be leaving the room because I knew he wouldn't beat me on the street. No, he would get me in the car, an alley, or any other place that would be semiprivate. However, leaving the room gave me a better chance of escaping another back handed slap.

Bob yelled at me the entire car ride. I was completely humiliated and just as angry at him for doing this to me.

"You're NOTHING, you hear me NOTHING! I should have put you on the bus the moment I met you." He went on and on, "The Regency doesn't want you anymore, that means I'm stuck with you! And if they EVER allow the other girls back, I wouldn't bring you back on a bet! You're WORTHLESS!"

"Was he ever going to stop, I thought as I sat between two of the girls with my head lowered. The others were also trying not to look at

Bob who could turn on them for any movement he felt was in defiance. I hoped we would get to wherever he was taking us soon, so I could get away from him and his vicious words.

"YOU'RE on the bus" He yelled "I'm through with you! You're getting on the first bus to Cleveland tomorrow morning!"

"Good", I shouted to myself, "Good! I don't want anything to do with you either!"

"You're gone, girl!" and with that the car stopped. "Get out of my car"

No one hesitated, we jumped out and headed straight into the bar. At this point, I was so angry I did not want to see him or the girls for the rest of the night. The only way I could do this was to turn as many tricks as I could. As soon as I entered the bar I scanned the dark room for some fool looking for a quick turn and went up to him.

"Hey," I said "You lookin' for a date?"

"Yes,"

I didn't even give him enough time to offer me a drink or ask me my name. I didn't care, I just wanted out of the bar and away from DeeDee and the others. "Let's go."

The rest of the night went just the same. I would just get back from one trick and be walking out with another. The money didn't really matter, I took them for whatever I could. Anything not to have to look at anyone the rest of the night.

Bob showed up at 3:30 to collect his money and get us back to the hotel to get some sleep.

"Where's Kim," Bob asked as he looked around the bar.

"I don't know, she's been gone all night." DeeDee answered.

"You think she run off?" Bob asked DeeDee as I walked in. "Kim!" he called.

I couldn't help myself, "WHAT?!"

He told me the night was over and he had come to pick us up. I didn't care and I didn't care if he knew how mad I was. "I'm still working!" and I walked up to a man who looked as if he had been there *all night. He smelled horrible, however, it wasn't his bathing habits I was after.*

"Hey," I leaned on the bar next to the man. "You lookin' for a date?" But before the man could belch his beer up, Bob took hold of my arm and said, "It's time to go, Kim"

I repeated, "I'm still working,"

He knew I was mad, but he also knew I had done some business and he wanted that money. "The bar is getting ready to close. The night is over."

I snarled as I turned to follow him and the others out to the car. Everyone was quiet not quite sure what was going to happen. One by one, Bob asked what each girl did. $40, $55, $45. When he came to DeeDee, she sat tall and handed him $75. DeeDee usually made the most, however not tonight. In the 3 ½ hours we had at the bar, I had one hundred, thirty-three dollars and sixty-three cents.

Bob laughed, DeeDee's shoulders dropped, and the others stared at me.

"One hundred, thirty-three dollars and sixty-three cents!" He laughed, "What'd you do? Turn a trick for his change?" I didn't answer him. I didn't care what he thought. It was actually some change I had from buying a pop.

As the others were wondering how I was able to make so much money in such a short time and DeeDee was sulking knowing Bob would not let me go anywhere now, I could think of only one thing, "Still think I'm not worth anything?"

Chapter 14

Bob told me Whitey put me on a trial period and if I successfully passed the two-week trial, I would be allowed to continue working out of his bar. Then, if I was good enough, Bob might be able to convince Whitey that the rest of the girls could do equally well.

Two-weeks later, Bob brought DeeDee in to work and within a month, the others were working there, as well.

Whitey's turned out to be an excellent trick bar. We could trust the tricks Whitey put us on, Whitey kept his word about telling us when a cop came in and he was so slick about it that it was next to impossible to see him telling anyone, but when a cop came in, not one girl took a trick. All business ceased until the cop left and Whitey gave the all clear.

Whitey casually made his way over to me and poured another drink. "Four to your right, in the blue jacket, he's a cop."

"Okay", I didn't need to look, I had seen him when he walked in. I sipped on my whiskey sour and wondered how long he would stay. It had been a slow night and time was running short. It always seemed a bit frustrating when vice came in. They knew who we were and what we were up to and we knew that they knew. There were times they would give up fast when they saw everything get quiet, other times you would think the cop was willing to wait us all out until last call. This was one of those times. Twenty minutes had past, and our young cop was still nursing his coke, patiently glancing around but not looking at the stage where the drag queens danced. He may have been afraid of the ribbing he would get should his team learn he was watching them dance.

I sat with Marie. Bob had recently pulled her and had given her to me to train.

Marie whispered to me "How long do cops usually stay?"

"Different times, but this guy doesn't seem to want to leave anytime soon." I snarled.

"Will Bobby get mad if we don't make any money? I mean, if he stays the rest of the night, what will happen?" Marie was a sweet girl but very fearful.

"We won't make any money. I have to do something." I answered.

"What can you do??"

Like I said, Marie was sweet, and she was very pretty, but she didn't have many kernels in her corncob. So, I just said "Watch." I got up from my stool and taking my drink, I went and sat at the stool next to the cop. Whitey looked over to me and I could tell he was not a happy camper. He had a look that clearly said, "WHAT IN THE HELL ARE YOU DOING." Obviously, I wasn't in the position to let Whitey in on my ruse so all I could do was avoid his angry gaze and his vain attempt to stop me.

"Hi," I innocently introduced myself.

He introduced himself as Henry.

"It's nice to meet you, Henry."

We made small talk for a little bit until he asked if I was working.

"Working!?" I gave a little dumb blond look then smiled and said. "Me? No, I'm not a transvestite and besides, I'm a horrible dancer. No, I don't work here. I'm just out having some fun is all."

He didn't seem to hear me, because he asked me how much money I wanted "for a half and half'. I nudged closer to his stool trying not to get too close but yet close enough that I could reach over and gently place my hand on his thigh. I smiled as I looked longingly into his "nervous newbie" eyes. "I'm…not…a…prostitute…" I softly assured him as my hand was moving slowly up his thigh.

"You…you're…um" he fumbled nervously looking for the words that would put him in control of the situation. Nevertheless, I was not giving him the time to think about anything other than what I wanted him to think.

"You…uh…wait" he tried again to establish authority. "You do it for money…right?"

"I…don't want…money…" his eyes grew wider as I got closer to him, "I just want to…" I whispered as I moved closer up to his ear, "have some…fun." I gently licked his baby soft ear lobe then took a firm hold of his crotch.

The newbie vice clearly horrified toppled off the stool sending it spinning and quickly made his exit. Business went back to business and I gaily strolled back to my seat and waited for Whitey.

Whitey was not impressed, nor did he gaily stroll. What he did do was ask me for clarification of my actions.

"What in the HELL were you doing?" He demanded. "You could have had us all locked up!"

I smiled and said, "Got rid of him, didn't I?"

Whitey did not return the smile, but he couldn't argue about it, so he went back to business as usual.

Bob announced, "There is going to be the largest convention to ever hit the city next week!"

It seemed as if news like this only excited one of us and that one person was Bob.

"Did you hear me girls??!" He was looking to see at least a spark of excitement. I mustered up as much as I could on such short notice.

"Yeah? Where are they supposed to be?" I asked.

Bob told us that the 100,000 Horny travelers were anticipated the following Tuesday and that they would be staying for three days. The convention that was to be at a posh hotel off Michigan Ave. was larger than any of us could imagine. I wondered if the city was big enough to accommodate that many visitors. It was.

Whiteys hadn't noticed much difference with the addition of 100,000 men in the city, but that could have been because the fun was not coming into Whiteys place. Walking into Whiteys that Tuesday night was like walking into the middle of a desert. You could almost see the vultures gliding around the sky as the stifling air lays stagnant and waste waiting for the bar to die!

It was truly depressing!

"Whitey!" He knew what we wanted.

"They will come! Just hang on, they will come in, I'm telling you!" He was telling us, but I don't think he actually believed it. I think he was hoping to have a sudden influx of thirsty and horny optometrists.

In frustration, I blurted out "This is ridiculous! It's ten o'clock and not one trick all night!"

I told the others I was tired of waiting for the tricks to come into Whiteys and I was going to go where they were. DeeDee said it would be a bad idea to leave now, "Especially if they all come and you're gone. Whitey will kick you out and then Bob will be really angry."

"He's going to be really angry if we stay here and nothing comes in. At least I could say I tried."

It felt like New Orleans all over again. DeeDee trying to pull rank and telling me I had better not go and me thinking she was stupid for not going.

"Just tell Whitey I felt sick and went home and if Bob comes in, tell him I went to the hotel they are at." and with the girls looking worried and DeeDee's rolling eyes I left and walked to the hotel that would have escorted me right out had they been able to see me.

When I walked into the lobby, I was overwhelmed by the number of men walking around, talking, laughing, and drinking. I wasn't sure where to go from there until a man approached me and said I looked lost.

"Well, not really, I heard…" I looked around "Are all of these guys from the convention?"

"Yup, 'cept the wimps that went to bed early." He had a slight southern accent. Not the eastern Kentucky drawl but more of a southern Ohio purr with a hint of Indiana pride. He went on to say there were a lot more of them in the lounge, restaurant and even more roaming through the halls.

"You're the first girl that has come in all night! We expected you all to come here." He explained that the management offered them "all kinds of free stuff" if they would stay at the hotel rather than go out.

Interesting…I was the only girl with one hundred THOUSAND men who were partying without their wives…interesting.

"Would you be interested in a date?" I asked.

This really excited him, "SURE! Look, if you're interested, I know a lot of guys who would be interested in a date, you can use one of the rooms and I'll get the word out and you can probably work all night long!"

Wow, this was great! It was a perfect set up with the corner on the market. No one expected the management to recommend they stay at the hotel, so everyone is street or bar tricking. Wow! I cornered it!

Once in the room, I sat down to call DeeDee. To my surprise, she wasn't interested. She wanted to stay at Whitey's.

"Besides, you're there. When you get done, come back to Whitey's and we will finish the night here."

Paul, the man with the slight southern accent, was true to his word, he had tricks coming to me all night long. I would hardly finish with one before another one was ready to go. They were coming so fast that Paul suggested I not even worry about getting dressed again. It was almost a relief.

I called DeeDee again but each call I made was met with the same answer, they are doing fine where they were.

"There is more than I can handle!" I finally admitted, but it didn't make any difference. It was unbelievable! The largest national convention in the history of Chicago was ripe for the picking and no one wanted to come!

They continued to come one after the other.

I thought I would try once more to get someone, anyone, even another pimps lady to come help. I decided to talk to Bob this time. "I'm getting sore, Bob, and there is still more"

"You're doing great, just keep going. DeeDee and the girls are getting busy now, too. How much have you made?"

"I don't know, I have another trick, I have to go."

I was putting the money in the bedside table, they were coming and going so fast I wasn't worried about anyone stealing from me.

"It's really beginning to hurt, I'm so dry." I said to myself. Lotion wasn't even helping much. All it did was help me to continue a little longer.

I'll use my soreness to make them think I'm coming. It will make them come faster.

I'm not sure I can continue much more.

My thoughts were solely on getting through the next trick, working through the pain. I wanted to stop so badly but I knew if I quit too early,

I would get in trouble. I had to keep going. Calling DeeDee or Bob was senseless, but I didn't know what else to do. Then when I thought I might be able to do it one more time, my body said "NO MORE" in raw form.

I was completely swollen shut and exhausted.

"Bob, I have to quit." It wasn't something I was in the habit of telling Bob. It wasn't something he was in the habit of accepting either.

"I'm totally closed off. I'm so swollen, it is absolutely impossible to do anything."

I suggested one more time that he send the girls down.

"I did," he admitted finally "They were stopped at the door. Evidently you snuck by them before they saw you. No ho can get in." Then he asked me again, how much I made.

DeeDee and Marie had made Eighty-five dollars, together, Nancy made ninety and I made Eight hundred, sixty-five dollars. I let Paul pay twenty-five instead of the thirty dollars everyone else paid for setting it all up.

PART II

Chapter 15

By the time I got home, all I could think about was a good soak in the tub. Maybe it will help the swelling and soreness, I thought to myself. I started the water running as I reached for the box of Epson salts.

"For Relief of Pain from Minor Sprains and Bruises"
"Laboratory Tested - Quality Guaranteed"

"Bruises, I would not doubt it in the least that I'm bruised." And with that I poured a hefty amount of it into the bath.

I slowly eased my overworked body into the warm water. It felt soothing against my skin as if I had slipped into a cloud of fine fur that carried me high above the world and away from tricks, pimps, and whores for however short of time it would afford me. I closed my eyes as I allowed the soothing warmth to continue to ease the night away. I'm not sure what prompted the vision I saw, maybe the sudden release of endorphins coupled with the relief of 'it is all over'.

There was a familiar sound of an old door creaked as it gave way slightly. A breeze possibly, no, that can't be right, there is no wind inside. Looking toward the sound, I found a plain wall with only a door to break up the overt loneliness of the white paint.

I noticed that the door had the image of a cross framed in the beveling that adorned the door. "I never noticed that before." I thought quizzically." Then I wondered if that image was it on the inside of the door as well? Interesting, Did the designer realized he had added this image of redemption or if it was purely accidental.

I heard that rusty hinge creak again and four slender fingers reached around the edge just above the doorknob. Then slowly a face began to emerge. A young teenage girl with innocent eyes peaked out looking around. When her eyes fell on mine, I recognized her. I knew who she was. She was someone I used to know from a long time ago. Her innocence was pure, however, there was worry and maybe even a little fear. Who is she, what does she want? I was struck dumb, without a voice, I just stared at her. Then,  suddenly my eyes were opened to her identity! She was me just a little while ago. Me, before I came to this wretched city of filth, deception and greed. Before I fell from grace through manipulations and promises, trickery and lies before I had become everything she wasn't.

In a soft whisper, I heard her ask, "Is it safe, yet?"

I saw both of my arms reach out toward her with a fierce need to protect and a force I had never felt before, I slammed the door closed and shouted, "NO"

The next day came too soon. I was still a bit sore but not as swollen. Still, I expected to be able to have the next day off, I felt I deserved it! I mean, Eight hundred, sixty-five dollars in, basically, half a night!!! Bob, though, expected a repeat of that night.

"Why aren't you getting dressed, Kim?" DeeDee asked in her "I'm the boss" voice.

I explained that I was still pretty swollen and sore, but DeeDee insisted I still had to go out. "Besides," she continued, "Bob wants you to go back to the hotel."

Back to the hotel… again?!… Another night like last night?? I don't think my body could take that kind of punishment.

Luckily, Bob walked in at that moment because I was biting my lip trying not to say something that would get me in trouble. Bob came into the apartment and immediately said "Kim, get dressed."

I quickly got dressed, I didn't know what he wanted me for and of course, I was not going to ask. I just knew at that moment it was not to drop me off at the hotel, it was still too early to go to work there.

"You are number one in the city, girl!" Bob told me in the car. "Everyone knows what you made last night!"

He went on to tell me what a huge deal it was and how no one in Chicago ever made that kind of money in one night of turning tricks. Bob continued talking the whole trip to a very fancy clothing store.

"Wow, it's not our regular haunt where any outfit you could find was no more than ten dollars, guaranteed."

I scanned the store windows as we walked up. Bob was still talking and as much as I was trying to listen, I couldn't help looking at all the beautiful clothes displayed on the mannequins. There were long gowns with sequins on beautiful lady mannequins and suits on the males. There was even a child mannequin holding a doll dressed in what looked like it might be a flower girl at a formal wedding. I'm not sure, but it was all so fancy.

We went in through the double glass doors into a showroom like I have never seen before. It reminded me of a Christmas trip downtown Cleveland I went on a couple of years ago.

It was the Christmas season and my brother and I along with a few friends took the rapid transit to downtown Cleveland. Matt had made it a tradition and had gone the last two years. It was my first year to go. Mom didn't want me to go when I was younger but now I was almost sixteen and I felt plenty old enough. Mom told Matt to watch over me and make sure I kept safe. It made me feel like a baby, but I didn't say anything I just scrunched my mouth and rolled my eyes. I just wanted to go on this wonderfully magical holiday excursion.

When we got off the train, it was much colder than it was at home and it would not be light for much longer, so we headed straight for Euclid Avenue where Christmas would shine the brightest. The street and store fronts sparkled with different colored lights and garland wrapped around the streetlamps. Twinkling silver and shiny gold decorated the trees, and in the store showcase windows winter continued with fake twinkling snow, huge sparkling snowflakes hanging from the ceilings and toys galore for the little ones to stare at from outside. Higbee's and May Company were favorites to visit and promised Christmas magic for all. We went from window to window doing a lot more window-shopping than anything else because we didn't have money for more than the rapid transit ride and dinner.

I wanted to stay forever, even with the bitter "booger freezing" weather. Nevertheless, it wasn't to be and after a wonderful meal of hamburgers and French fries, we headed back home in time for our ten o'clock curfew.

I wondered if I would ever feel that way again. Sometimes I would look out the window in the early mornings and see all the people headed out to their jobs for the day. Some sipping on a cup of coffee trying to beat the 8:00 morning rush while others shaving as they raced to make the morning meeting with the crew.

At 4:30 in the afternoon, I would see those same people headed home for dinner with the wife and kids, or the empty apartment to sit in front of the television with a TV dinner until the 10:00 news ended and

they went to sleep, a bed that was meant for rest, not work. For those
people, the lucky ones, the bed was a welcoming oasis that carried their
day into the morning when they would wake up to a welcoming sun. For
me, the bed was anything but an oasis. It felt as though beds were
everywhere, no living areas, no dining tables, just beds, a constant
reminder of performing an act against my will as many times a night as
I could. Even when the work night was over, I wasn't safe from having
to "perform" once more, only this time with Bob. I longed for an
ordinary life where my bed was a welcomed site, my safe haven, one of
warm solitude.

Bob led me straight to a rack of beautiful leather outfits. It almost
seemed like he knew exactly what he wanted to show me. As if he had
been there before, preparing for this moment. I looked at the rows of
hangers, each one set on the metal bar with the exact same distance to
the next, each perfectly supporting a fresh style. Some of the outfits had
real fur collars, others without any fur at all, but each just as beautiful as
the next.

I was dumbfounded, I didn't understand. I looked to Bob who was
standing beside me with the biggest grin on his face. "You earned it,
girl. Whatever you want."

"ANY thing?" I asked in utter shock. "Anything I want in this entire
store?"

"You can have whatever you want." and he thumbed through a few
hangers and pulled out an absolutely gorgeous white leather pantsuit
with a matching form fitting long sleeved jacket. "How about this one?"
I could hear the excitement in his voice. "Or this?" and he held up
another suit with a skirt. I didn't pay too much attention to his second
choice. My heart was pounding for that white pantsuit.

I gingerly took the pantsuit and held it up to see it better. The white
leather was baby soft and moved easily in my hand. Bob said
something, but I didn't hear, I was too enamored with the thick white
fox fur collar.

"Do you want to try it on?"

In the dressing room, the jacket hugged my body as if it was tailored specifically for me and the pants were snug and fit perfectly. I stared at myself in the mirror, turning to see it from all sides.

"I wanted it" I whispered to myself, stroking the collar." I earned it, I want this so, so badly." Bob had said not to look at the price tag, but I couldn't resist, it was two hundred forty-nine dollars and ninety-nine cents. My jaw fell to the floor as the price loomed.

"He did say I could get it, and he said the cost did not matter." I reasoned. "But two hundred forty-nine dollars and ninety-nine cents, I have never even dreamed of having something so extravagant in my life!"

As I stepped out of the dressing room, Bob was waiting to see me.

"You look gorgeous!" he said.

I felt a little embarrassed, but I did feel beautiful. Even the salesman smiled in approval. Then, at the very same time, Bob was asking if I wanted it, I felt a twinge of fear and a warning. It came to me as many warnings had come to me in the past, it was a quiet whisper of a voice warning me to turn aside, take another road, and go in a different direction because danger is near.

"You will pay sorely for that pant suit if you get it. Accept nothing."

I knew within my soul that it meant if I accepted anything of value that it would come back to me with a haunting degradation of a severe beating for something and that I had not deserved. I never knew where the warnings came from, but I had learned a long time ago that it was wise to listen.

On the corner of Clark and Belmont was a restaurant that I loved going to. Just a little greasy spoon joint with booths that lined the windows looking out onto Belmont Ave and a long bar with stools should you be eating alone or stopping in for a quick cup of coffee. I liked to sit at the far end in a booth. Usually, someone was with me and I would order the same thing every time. Grilled cheese and burnt French fries.

I had to tell the waitress to burn the fries otherwise I got pale and limp potatoes that were mushy and no good. I wanted crisp fries and my first visit I sent them back three times before I told her to burn 'em.

"Look, its grilled cheese and burnt French fries." The waitress would say when we came in. It made me smile that she recognized me.

This one particular evening Sammy and Terry were going with me. It was nice to have three of us, however as we came to the Clark Street and Halsted cross, I felt that familiar whisper telling me to go up Halsted to Belmont and over to Clark. I wondered why and was immediately granted a "wow" explanation. For some reason, if I went up Clark Street, I would get a beating for something, but if I took the longer, out of the way, route I would be safe.

The girls thought I was being stupid but agreed to go down Halsted. Then I was stopped in my tracks, it was as if I walked straight into an unseen wall.

"What now?" Sammy asked.

The still little voice told me that Terry must take Clark Street. It was absurd! Why do we have to take two different routes to the same place? Terry felt it was all a trick to lose her.

"No, I swear." I tried to alleviate her doubts, however, it was not to be. Terry insisted on all three of us going the same route, Clark Street.

"No way," I protested, "When I feel a premonition, I will not ignore it. Not anymore. I've seen them come true over and over", I didn't know what else to call it and anyway, premonition seemed better than saying I was "hearing voices". Continuing I advised Terry that she really should go down Clark and Sammy could go that way as well, if she wanted to but I'm taking Belmont and with that I began walking.

Sammy and Terry would not listen to me. I felt very fearful for Terry, but my hands were tied.

With a shrug, I said "I warned you."

The next morning, after a tiring night of turning tricks, Terry asked Bob if she could take Pepper, my malamute, for a walk. It had become their nightly routine and although Pepper was my dog, I could see he loved to go for these daily walks. Terry asked if I wanted to tag along, but I was not interested. "Maybe next time."

This day, however, was different. They were back much sooner than usual, and it was obvious that Terry had run into trouble. Bob had secretly followed Terry and she met up with a young man. Bob beat her. Terry ran the next day.

I wonder now, if these warning premonitions as I called them, were angels watching over me and maybe God was testing me by sending Terry and me in opposite routes.

To Bob's surprise as well as the disappointment of the salesman, I turned down his offer of buying the gorgeous, one of a kind, I'll never get another chance to own such beauty, white leather pant suit with a white fox fur collar and would accept nothing else in its place.

I held my head low as I told him I wouldn't accept anything. Once in the car, Bob asked, "Why didn't you want the pant suit?"

"Oh," I didn't really know what to say. "Where would I wear it?"

-You see, Bob, it's like this; I seem to get these little feelings or premonitions of what could happen. And, well, this time it said you were going to beat the crap out of me and berate me in front of the others because that is what you like to do!-

"It was too expensive." I hung my head because I knew it was not as much as I had made the night before.

"Yes, but you earned it."

All I could do was shrug and say, "I don't need it."

When we got back to the apartment, DeeDee and Marie had been waiting for me.

"Hurry up. Let's go."

I turned to Bob in the vain hope that he had changed his mind and I could have the night off. Instead, he told the others he wanted me to go back to the hotel in hopes of a repeat of last night.

Turning down the most beautiful outfit I had ever seen didn't even give me a single night off. Turning all those tricks until I was raw and completely swollen shut, did not entitle me to a free night. Making Eight hundred sixty-five dollars in one night, more than any one ho up to that point in the city of Chicago had ever made, did not grant me even one single night off, not one.

Bob dropped me off on the corner by the elegant hotel and raced off to parts unknown. As I entered the front doors, it felt odd. It was quiet, not at all like the night before. The lobby held only a handful of people who were casually walking around or sitting on the luxurious davenports. They were just too fancy to call couches, even though that is what they were.

I must have looked lost.

"Excuse me miss", He was a professional looking man, stood straight and walked with his arms down swinging slightly with every generous step he took towards me.

Semi respectfully, he asked if he could help me.

"Well, no." Then thinking about it, I said, "Yesterday, there were so many people here. Did they all leave?"

His gracious attitude turned as he informed me, "They went to another hotel." I wasn't sure if his demeanor changed because his business left, or he realized why I was asking and what I was doing there.

He would not tell me where they went or why, but he did ask me if I had a room before "inviting" me to "leave the premises immediately", before he called security who would remove me from the building. Not being a hard ass, I felt walking out under my own steam was the better choice.

I was surprised to find Whitey's as quiet as the hotel. DeeDee, Sammy and Marie were sitting in our regular seats at the end of the long oddly shaped bar, Whitey was wiping down a section of the bar as usual, more than likely a glass had left a ring on the counter. This always prompted a good scrubbing of three or four bar stool spots. Whitey never did anything without making it a bigger job. He liked his bar clean.

I asked if there had been anything at all this evening. DeeDee sneered and said, "Hardly anything, just like last night."

I couldn't believe what I heard. Last night when I was begging for help, they were sitting here not doing anything?!

"Nothing?" I wanted to be sure that I heard correctly. "Nothing, last night?" They simply shrugged their shoulders without looking up.

"Then why the hell didn't you guys come to the hotel?" I was getting angry now.

"Bob wanted us to stay here in case some of them came here." It was as if it didn't mean a thing one way or another to them.

I couldn't argue about it, it appeared that Bob was the one holding everyone back. I wondered later if Bob was acting out of fear of Whitey and his rule of always showing up, so decided to tell me that stupid story that they couldn't get into the hotel.

About a week later, I was busted and while sitting in the overcrowded cell, one of the ladies called to me.

"Hey, Ho!" I looked to see the skank, as did most of the other ladies, "Who yo' man?"

"Bob Roberts"

"Bob Roberts!?" she blurted, "From the near north side?"

"Yeah", I wondered what she was getting at.

"Wuz yo name?" she asked eagerly.

"Kim"

"I KNOW YOU! I hear'd o' you." her eyes were open wide with a big smile that made me feel like some sort of celebrity. "My man tell'd me bout ch'a. You that ho what made all that money in one night!"

The other Ho's were looking at me now all asking me questions. The discussion lasted about fifteen minutes before my mood dropped and I wondered.

"Is this what I am going to leave as a legacy? Turning enough tricks in a night to make over $800? Is that going to be my claim to fame, the Chicago hooker who screwed more men in one night than any other hooker in Chicago's history? Is that my fifteen minutes of fame?

I thought back to my childhood when I wanted to be the next Mary, bringing Jesus back as he promised. I was about six years old. Now I wondered if there was a God.

Chapter 16

DeeDee and the others were surprised when they saw me coming into Whitey's.

I expected DeeDee to ask me why, but it was Sammy who spoke up first, "Why are you not at the hotel?"

Hushed by DeeDee, she turned to me and asked if I was feeling better loud enough for Whitey to hear if he was listening. We never knew how good Whitey's hearing was or if someone might say something thereby getting us all kicked out for breaking one of Whitey's "you're out" violations.

"If you work here, you work here, got it? You don't turn any tricks outside of this place, if you do, you're out."

I sat next to DeeDee and leaned over so Sammy could also hear. "They moved somewhere else and I couldn't find out where. I also got kicked out of the hotel." DeeDee said she heard there were a few girls working the convention who were not very discrete which was most likely why they were moved to another hotel. That seemed a little obsessive to me, but then providing free booze and snacks to stop them from going out into the city seems just as erratic

Just then in walks a prospective end to a quiet. Neither Sammy nor DeeDee showed any interest and told me if I wanted to try, to go ahead. Marie just continued nursing her drink.

"Someone has to." I mumbled. If Bob walked in or Whitey spotted us all sitting together ignoring a prospective trick, we would all catch it big time.

I walked over to the average height, average weight, average trick and leaned in close to ask if he minded me sitting in the stool next to him.

"Not at all, have a seat", He liked what he saw. So did I, that is, if the money was right.

Whitey brought me a drink and counted the cost of the drink out of the tricks change he had left on the bar.

As I took a sip of my drink from the stir-straw, Jake, as he called himself, smiled as he took a sip from his rock glass, bypassing the tiny straw.

Our conversation consisted of simple things, the weather, yesterday's weather, and what someone said tomorrows weather would be before finally, if he was looking for a date.

We had been talking for a few minutes and established that he was, indeed, looking for a little fun. It was then that Marie squeezed her way in between us rudely inviting herself into our conversation. My trick became more and more interested in her, quickly pushing me back into the position of the third wheel.

Coming to an arrangement, Marie turned to me with a smile "You don't mind, do you Kim?"

"No," what else could I say? "That's fine", Truthfully, I was livid.

"Where does she get off taking a trick away from me?" I thought as I walked back to where the others were, who saw the whole thing.

DeeDee saw the anger in my eyes. I was rarely angry, but this was stealing my status with Bob that I had worked so hard to achieve not to mention recent events. It's a difficult thing to understand why I wanted to turn as many tricks as I did and why I didn't work with the "Well, it all goes to Bob anyway." attitude some of the girls in the past have had.

It might have appeared that I wanted to be with everyone in town. As if I was the biggest slut, Bob had ever pulled. However, the truth was that before I came to Chicago, I was known for never wanting to do any of that. I had a reputation of being "frigid", and "prude", however, to help ensure less beatings, is to bring in as much money as possible. It creates trust and Bob then sees me as a devoted ho, something that I knew I would eventually need.

This trick was the third one that Marie had blatantly stolen right out from my grasp. Twice the other night and then now. Everyone knew what she was doing, even Whitey was seeing her as the little skank she was.

"Kim, are you gonna' let her get away with that? She's waiting for you to make the mark and then taking him away from you!" Whitey appeared as angry about it as I felt.

"Nope," I mumbled "Not anymore." Whitey knew I planned to put a stop to her trick pilfering. The problem was, how.

Marie was appearing more and more comfortable with it as well. I can forgive, but I had reached my "seventy times seven" limit. As Whitey went back to wiping down the counter tops, I began to steam. I could actually feel my blood pressure rising and seething reaching to the point of explosion. I was reeling with anger at Marie's cockiness, then I felt what everyone was probably thinking. "What is she going to do? She looks as if she is going to blow." I considered going back to the apartment however, that was against one of Whitey's rules.

"You must stay until the end of the night, leaving only with a trick and returning immediately." If you don't, you're out.

I decided to take a deep breath and deal with it later. However, the intake of air only fueled my fury, which was building into rage.

I knew I needed to calm down and my present attempt was not working. I had to find a safe haven of solitude in which I could calm myself. I got up from my stool and without thinking quickly made my way to the bathroom. I stepped into the small room that held only a toilet and a small 1950's style sink. I closed the door behind me, took two steps toward the far wall, spun around and with the roar of an angry lion fighting to maintain his territory, I put my four inch heal through the door. When I saw the damage I did, my first thought was for my own skin.

"What will Whitey say, what will he tell Bob, what will Bob say?" and, "Oh, crap." But my anger still reeled inside of me. I flung the door open to find a crowd of concerned people clamoring around. They were trying to see if I had any injuries and asking what happened. I pushed my way through the storm of bodies as I shouted, "I'm FINE!"

In the swift steps I had adopted in my anger, I found myself becoming concerned of what the repercussions would be for my transgressions. I began to slow my stride as I was considering the punishment I was looking at when I reached the apartment and saw Bob.

"This is bad" I concluded. "Bob will have a cow, I'll be lucky if I live through it." First, I weighed out what Bob is going to do then what Whitey is going to do and then the beating I would receive for the infringement on Whitey's house rules. Not only did I kick a hole through the bathroom door, but I also walked out in the middle of the evening! One of Whitey's "you're out." violations.

I stopped a safe distance from the apartment, safe enough should Bob be there. I wasn't ready to answer a barrage of questions. I thought better of my actions and turned around.

Right now, Marie's antics was safer to deal with, anyway, I had to stop this once and for all. I'll deal with Bob and his anger later.

I felt a bit self-conscious walking into Whitey's after damaging the bathroom door and wondered if I would catch it from Whitey. I looked at the hole my big foot made and cringed to myself as I wondered how much it would cost to replace. Would it cost a beating or just getting yelled at?

Slowly sitting down in my usual spot and looked around at the various patrons. Everyone seemed to be back to business as usual. It was as if nothing had happened. The only difference was the hole in the ladies' room. DeeDee was talking to a trick as she sat with her arms on the bar holding her whiskey sour in both hands. She looked up as I sat and quietly asked if I was okay.

"Yeah," I answered with a discrete scowl. "But don't count on Marie being okay later." There was no answer.

Whitey walked up and without a word, placed a drink in front of me. Gingerly I reached for it with both hands. "Thanks." I sucked both of my lips in so I could bite them together. I had found in times like this it was better to keep my mouth shut.

It wouldn't take long before Marie returned. She appeared happy, almost proud of her accomplishment. She went to the bar and gave Whitey his cut. Whitey pocketed the bills. Marie walked over to us and sat down next to me. Still angry, I took a long look into her eyes. Marie's smile slowly disappeared before she looked at the others and turned back to me. "What's wrong?"

I stood up from my bar stool and as calm as I could, I said "Com'ear".

Now I saw the fear realized in her as the olive tone in her face turned stark white.

"Where?" she fearfully asked. She knew what she had done, and she knew she had run out of chances.

"Just, com'ear" I repeated.

I didn't look around, but I would not have been surprised to see all eyes on us.

Marie asked again, where we were going. My anger was growing, I could feel the heat rising from my scalp like the steam coming up from a pot of hot water boiling on the stove.

"Either you come with me now or I will drag you. Makes no difference to me." I warned.

Marie decided she better get down from her stool. Looking back to the others, it was obvious they were not coming to her rescue. As we made our way along the stools and tables, I could see, this time the chatter quieted, and the eyes watched to see where we were going and what was going to happen to the little trick thief. No one offered help and the further down the bar we got, the more fear filled Marie's eyes.

We got to the bathroom where I told her to "get in". Her reply was almost in tears as she asked why. "GIT IN" I demanded. She tried to say no, but it simply fueled my anger. She could see in my eyes, she had no choice. Every muscle in her body was jumping now as she backed up to the tiny room that was meant more for relief than anger and fear.

"NO!" Marie continued. Her fear was exactly what I wanted in order to make my point, but I wasn't done.
"Get...your...ass...in...the...bathroom, now!" I said through my clinched teeth and fiery eyes.

"I don't want to!" Marie tried once more.

I took a hold of her arm and pushed her in, closing the door behind me. As I reminded her of the three times she decided to steal my tricks and that it was to stop here and now, she carefully maneuvered herself over to the door. There wasn't enough room for her to open it without me stopping her, but the fact that she did this impressed me.

"Now, turn around," I instructed. The music continued to play loudly behind the closed bathroom door. Marie began to plead, saying she won't take another trick from me. "You're right there!" I said "Now, turn the hell around and look down."

As she turned slowly fully expecting multiple blows, she suddenly saw the hole in the door.

Quickly standing straight up and turning around in shock she exclaimed "Oh my GOD, What Happened!!?"

In anger, I told her if she had stayed in the bar one minute longer than she did after stealing another trick from me, the hole would have been in her head and not the bathroom door.

Exiting the bathroom, I saw most everyone quickly turn back to their drinks pretending they weren't being nosey, but it was obvious, almost funny, how everyone flipped around to their drinks and conversation. Whitey, on the other hand, continued to watch. Marie left and as I took my seat at the bar, Whitey delivered a drink and said with pride "That's the way to do it." He then smiled the first and the last smile I would ever see on Whitey's face. I forced myself to smile, even though I was still feeling a bit angry.

No one seemed to care or even wonder why Marie left the bar.

We met up with Bob as he was leaving the apartment and we were walking home. He asked where Marie was. DeeDee jumped in and excitedly explained what had been going on and what I did about it. Bob looked at me, "Really?" I nodded my head as I readied myself for a beating, but Bob just turned around and said "Well," as he Shrugged, "She probably ran."

Marie was gone. I guess I scared her too much. Whitey fixed the bathroom door, and nothing was ever mentioned about that night again.

Chapter 17

Spring had an innocence about her that you only see in the eyes of the very young. When we met her, she lived with her mother one floor below us. She always seemed to be around, either standing downstairs by the front desk, by the elevator, or sitting in the hallway on our floor. We all wondered what she was doing and would say hi because she has become such a familiar sight to the building. It wasn't too long before the only place we saw her was on our floor halfway between the elevator and our apartment. Her face would light up each time we crossed paths.

Spring, although living in such a horrible, dirty apartment building viewed life as an adventure meant to explore anyway you could, come what may. For some reason, Spring saw prostitution as another adventure to explore and possibly a way out of the poverty she was living in with her mother.

Spotting Bob one day, she decided to ask if she could join his stable and work for him. She promised devotion and profit for Bob if she could only be with us. However, despite her desires to join us, she was still a virgin and....

"I'm ten."

His reply came with a smile and a promise. "Come find me in a few years and we'll see what we can do."

Although Spring was sad, she accepted his answer with a promise of finding him again when she was older. It was all but forgotten.

Spring went back to doing what ten-year old's do best, we moved out of that apartment on Dearborn to work out of the hotel, once again. We truly never expected to hear from her again, after all, who in their right mind would truly ask once, let alone twice. Her prepubescent view of prostitution would surely change once she was older.

Then, later after we had moved out of the murphy bed apartment, she showed up. I'm not sure who found who, but here she was.

Bob had his arm around this beautiful girl with a smile and a twinkle in his eye. "You all remember Spring?" He announced, "She's joining us."

She was eleven years old.

It seemed that things were getting more and more dangerous and it seemed to begin with Spring. Then there was the time I came back to find Bob, DeeDee and someone I was not familiar with at the table with a mountain of cocaine they were "cutting"! That was the first time I thought to myself, "Shit! We are all going to prison for drugs." Luckily, after Bob had made a sale to a dealer, he decided drugs were too risky to deal with. No pun intended.

Soon, Bob pulled a girl by the name of Lola who he had picked up at the bus station. DeeDee and I found out about her age one night when she said she had a secret but made us promise not to tell Bob that she told us. He had told her not to say anything to us, but, as she said, "I just think you have a right to know."

She was twelve years old.

Bob started coming to the apartment with various men he called his honcho's. Usually, they were gone relatively quick, except for one.

Bill, a tall, lanky man with messy blond hair and a twinkle in his eyes that followed a smile that would knock you flat. His teeth were bad, really, really bad. He followed Bob in the apartment and was introduced as Bob's "very good friend." This upset DeeDee tremendously. I wasn't exactly sure why, we had seen many other men that Bob brought to the apartment and I anticipated this one would be gone just like the others.

"Honcho's, as well as girls came and went on a regular basis. If you think about it" I said, "prostitution has a high rate of turning over." I smiled at my joke before glancing over to see if Tom was back yet. He had gotten up a few minutes ago, I assumed it was to go to the bathroom. I thought he would have been back by now, "but men do seem to take longer in the bathroom than any three women in a row. I suppose that's why some people keep magazines in their bathroom."

Coming and going was just the way it was, but what was really interesting, however, was that they all left just like Tom did when he went to the bathroom, without a word.

Just then, in walks Tom with what folks used to call a "Dagwood" sandwich. He must have gone behind me to the kitchen when I wasn't looking.

That sandwich was piled high with just about everything we had in the fridge including, mayonnaise, mustard, and catsup. There was, as the ad goes "Two all-beef patties, special sauce, lettuce...tomato...pickles...something, something, something. I could never get that list of ingredients down right. Whatever, I wondered if he was planning to eat the whole thing himself or if he planned on sharing it with me. Tom licked his lips in anticipation, then tried to open his mouth wide enough for a bite.

Nope, can't do it. I smiled again at his elevated expectations and went back to my mending.

Chapter 18

I had returned to the apartment to go to the bathroom before heading out again. No one was at home.

I liked walking into a quiet apartment. There was no DeeDee to question me about something, no Bob to wanting a quickie. It was just quiet.

The place was a mess, as usual. Laundry piled so high, I wondered if we were going to have to use a sheet to carry it five blocks to the laundry mat again. That was horrible and we all agreed we would not let the laundry get that bad again. Besides, when it did, Bob usually flipped out at how messy the place was.

I stepped over the laundry, which I estimated not to be as bad as last time. "Eh, we can wait another couple of days."

The bathroom door was closed but, believing I was the only one home, I flung the door open to find Bill standing with an elastic band around his upper left arm with one end gripped tight between his teeth.

He was just as shocked to see me as I was to see him. He was just about to plunge a syringe into the bulging vain in his arm when I walked in.

"Oh shit", we said simultaneously.

I was in shock, I would never have thought he was an addict. "I'm so sorry, Kim" He said with the band still clinched between his yellowed teeth. "I never wanted any of you to know about this, especially you."

I never did like the idea of drugs, especially when it came to needles.

"No, I'm sorry" I said backing out. "I should have knocked. I just, just…" I stammered.

"I'll be out in a few minutes." He said as I closed the door feeling very embarrassed.

Standing in the center of the mountain of dirty laundry, thinking over what I had just seen. I don't think I even felt the wadded-up clothing under my feet. Bill was shooting up something that was in that small syringe, I suspected it was heroin. My thoughts went to DeeDee.

I asked myself, "Is Bills addiction what upset DeeDee so bad or..." I thought, "Is it possible that Bob's 'special friend' was gay?" I quickly dismissed the notion because that would mean that Bobby was bi-sexual!

The idea of Bob being gay sickened me, but "He had spent some time in prison before." And I had heard that the men rape each other. Maybe he got to like it, the fight and then the rape. It was, after all, his favorite style.

"Wow," something suddenly occurred to me, "Maybe, that's why he likes sex after beating someone!"

Bill seemed to hang around for quite some time. I had actually gotten to enjoy his company, even though I knew he dealt with a 'jones'. He treated us with respect, as if we were real people, not whores, bitches, or things that didn't matter. It was nice, and the bonus was we didn't have to perform for him. In fact, Bobby seemed less interested in us while Bill was around. I hoped he would hang around for a while.

A month or so later, Spring and I came into the apartment to change clothes when we heard a horrible wail. It was a sound like a string makes when it is pulled through a hole in the skin of a drum. A sound that would send shivers up and down your spine.

We looked at each other as we wondered what that horrible sound was. Spring wanted to leave but I wanted to see if someone was hurt. "If someone is hurt, I want to help if we can." I insisted.

We entered the apartment with reserved hesitation, taking one cautious step at a time as if we were feeling for steppingstones while making our way through a bog of quicksand. We were afraid of what we would find. Our thoughts reeled.

"It's coming from the bathroom." I said,

"Should we knock?" asked Spring.

"I don't know... maybe we should just go in." I continued before I remembered walking in on Bill. The wailing began to sound somewhat hoarse, like an animal that had been roaring for his mate that lay in the road run over and dying. Then the wailing slowed a down and we began hearing water running.

"Is someone in the bath, is someone dying?" our minds were searching for some sort of rational explanation for the terrible sound. For a split second, I wondered if it was Bob and he had been stabbed or shot.

I gently knocked before peeking in the door. I saw DeeDee sitting on the toilet pouring water over a man's shoulders and back. The faucet was spilling out steaming water into the tub as a naked man sat hunched over holding his stomach and began screaming again, in a debilitating howl of excruciating agony.

DeeDee was desperately trying to comfort the man. She looked up and I saw a pain in her eyes that only wanted out. That didn't want to be where she was at that moment. She wanted only to walk away from this man's agonizing screams of pain.

"Bill?" I said in utter shock, the wailing came from Bill. "What happened, why is he like that? What's going on?" My question rolled out only adding to the noise. My questions looked for answers that would not be answered with anything other than "Go out, get out." from DeeDee.

Bill, those horrible sounds were coming out of Bill and I didn't know why. We tried to sit on the couch, but his wailing sent bolts of anxiety through my body and I had to leave.

A few days later, I saw Bill packing a few things in a suitcase. Bob had told him to leave. He would not support his habit anymore and he wouldn't deal with his DT's again.

"Sorry, Kim" He said as he passed by me and out the door.

That scene, that horrible night seeing Bill suffering with the DT's was more than I could handle. Once again, my psyche took control and told me it was a scene from a movie about an athlete that died from a painful cancer.

It was not unusual for Bob to take DeeDee to the bus station in search young runaway girls to pull. Runaways are easy to spot if you know what to look for. They will be sitting alone, looking rather lost and scared. They may or may not have a backpack or nothing but the clothes on their back. Bob could spot them a mile away, the lost and hungry. It was those too young to be away by their self, running away from some trauma going on in their young life.

Turning around to face DeeDee, Bob looked her square in the eyes and quietly asked, "Do you see her?"

DeeDee scanned the large open room of men, women, and families with young children trying desperately to see exactly who Bob was talking about. Banned from the bus stations, Bob was able to discretely enter for short periods of time but had to leave quickly before being spotted by security.

"Where is she?" DeeDee asked.

A bit upset that she was unable to easily spot who he was talking about, Bob took a deep breath in through his now flared nostrils and with wide eyes and impatient clenched teeth, he spoke slowly. "She...is...on...the...bench...behind me about halfway down."

Since they were standing a fair distance from any bench, DeeDee traced each bench behind Bob, halfway down until she spotted the short, blond, girl biting her nails.

"The one sitting just past a boy with a jean jacket on?" Somehow, Bob knew the boy and girl were not together. Although, it wouldn't matter either way, Bob would split them up and get rid of the boy, just as he did many times before. Bob turned just enough to get a look at her with his peripheral vision. "She's wearing blue jeans and a pink halter top."

The boy got up and went over to his mother leaving the young waif alone on the bench thereby providing Bob with prideful confirmation of his intuitive power.

"Yeah, I see her" DeeDee said as Bob turned to go outside. Security had entered the transient room but had not yet spotted him.

DeeDee casually strolled close to the young prospect. As she reached as close to the girl as she dared, DeeDee looked around the room as if she were looking for someone. As if she was expecting someone who hadn't shown up yet.

Acting as though she was frustrated, DeeDee plopped down on the bench like a rag doll and announced "MAN, I'm hungry." Once more, DeeDee glanced around allowing her eyes to fall on the young runaway. "Hey, you got any money I can borrow so I can get a candy bar or something?"

The girl takes a quick fearful look at DeeDee and replies exactly what she was hoping. "No."

"Good," DeeDee thought, "She's broke". It always made it easier if the girl didn't have any money. It typically meant she was stranded. Now all she had to do was to convince her to go out of the bus station and find Bob. He always said. "If she comes out of the station, I got her." and it was true.

"Crap!" DeeDee announces as she again looks around for her imaginary friend.

"My friend is supposed to come and pick me up. He said he could get me a job modeling." DeeDee paused then as if talking to herself, "Hey, maybe...where is that asshole...maybe, if he ever gets here, he'll buy me something to eat. I haven't eaten since Louisville." DeeDee paused again and reached into her pocket, "I need a smoke."

"Me too" The girl said not really intending for DeeDee to hear, but DeeDee was listening very close.

DeeDee continued to talk about this and that, periodically looking around for her supposed friend who was supposed to meet her. DeeDee was a pro at working people and was soon able to pull the runaway out of her shell. She was able to learn her name, where she was from, where she was going, how she was going to go. She smoked, drank, had a boyfriend she was intimate with, but they had broken up because he cheated on her and even more information than that. Then before she even knew what happened, she had been convinced into coming outside where Bobby had been sitting "waiting" and ready to play his part.

"Well, there you are." raising his arms for a welcome to the big city hug.

DeeDee continues with just as much astonishment. "I KNEW it, I was inside waiting for you when I began to wonder if you were waiting out here!"

"I thought I was supposed to meet you outside." Bob said apologetically. "Who is this?"

"Oh," DeeDee acting as if she had forgotten about the girl. "This is a...my new friend, Becky. I met her inside the terminal, and we are both starved! You got any money?"

That was Bobby's cue to flash his wad of cash he always had tucked in his front pocket. A thick stack of bills neatly folded in half with a fifty-dollar bill right on top. There were so many bills it was impossible for Bob to use a money clip so he would put a rubber band around them so they wouldn't slip apart.

"I think I have a little." He said as he fanned the bills.

DeeDee could get a girl almost, as well as, she could find a trick. She and Bobby went out many times in search of the young, vulnerable and unaware. I, on the other hand, was extremely inept at the time-honored art of pulling. When Bob decided it was time for DeeDee to pass the torch, so to speak, I just couldn't do it, I would go with him and try to do my part, but I had a horribly difficult time inviting any unsuspecting girl into a life fraught with sex, money, fear and violence. It was one thing for me to become who I needed to in order to survive but quite another to trick an innocent child to do this shit. I wanted to tell them to go away, go home, call your parents, do anything, just stay away from this life. Pulling was one thing I just could not do.

The bus station came to be a source of depression to me. In fact, depression was becoming more and more prevalent. I seemed to withdraw into my thoughts more and more, trying in vain to find some sort of escape. It was becoming harder to find each day.

Sitting at the dining room table I felt myself sinking down into far away thoughts of nothing, I reached for a small package that was sitting on the table. Deep into my own silent obscurity, the object did not mean anything. Its identity was insignificant, its sole purpose at the moment was to provide my hands with something to hold onto. Something that did not have a hold of me. It was soft, like a mattress was supposed to be. My thumb ran over the smooth outer covering. I knew I wielded the power to smash it in my hand, and I considered doing just that, but I

didn't have the mental strength or the will. Then my eyes drifted
mindlessly away from the object in my hands and fell on another object.
This object was shiny and thin, maybe the length of a toothpick. I had
seen people hold them in their mouth twirling it around and around, but
I couldn't remember who. "Maybe it is a toothpick," I thought to
myself. "No, toothpicks are dull, made out of. of...wood. This is not
wood, wood is not shiny. It doesn't matter" I concluded. This object was
silver not wood. It was also pointy at one end. I wondered if it would go
into the other object. Was it as strong as it looked? What would it feel
like to plunge this shiny thing into the other thing that seemed so soft
and smooth? What would happen if I united them in such a bazaar and
cruel manner? I decided I wanted to know what it felt like and began to
slowly push the thin sharp, thing into the other thing. It went in so
smooth, not at all as if you might thing but smooth, easy, without any
effort at all. I became fascinated as I slowly plunged the...the... Then I
realized what it was. It was a needle. Each time the needle penetrated
the object a sense of "awe" followed. Nothing else mattered, nothing
else existed, it was just me, the needle and.... The item revealed itself, it
came into recognizable view and what it was ...was...DeeDee's
cigarettes! Quickly, I put the package of Kool cigarettes and needle
down and collected myself as I moved away from the table.

I felt as though I was slipping away. The depression that came over
me quite some time ago, was rapidly increasing and becoming harder
and harder to keep hidden. The constant threat of getting beat, going to
jail, police raids, not turning enough tricks or making enough money to
satisfy Bob's thirst was not the life I wanted. I felt as if I was alone, in a
small room with no windows or doors; only dark clouds that hung from
the ceiling threatening to pour down drops of icy water. I was forgetting
who I was and how I came to be here. I had relinquished any faith I had
in the past in humankind and the faith in my God was gone as well. I
was simply a nameless thing whose body was treated with no dignity,
no respect. Just like the girl that died in that hotel room when Carmen,

Matt, Bear and I first came to town. And just like her, I felt disposed of quietly.

A pounding on the front door not only startled us, but also sent a bolt of sharp electricity straight up my spine, exploding out the top of my head. For a moment, I thought I would pass out.

Was it a raid? It wouldn't have been the first time. DeeDee got up and quietly made her way to the window. The pounding came again only this time we heard a man's voice demanding us to open the door.

DeeDee peeked out the curtains to see who was standing on the stoop. It was Bob! DeeDee ran to open the front door as quickly as possible. Bob was barely standing holding himself in an upright position with the aid of the doorframe. He was bloody and bruised. One eye swollen shut, it looked as if there was a golf ball behind his eyelids. The other eye, though no visible swelling, bore the unmistakable sign of a hemorrhage within the white part of the eye. His lips protruded on his left side with a line of blood that matched his lower teeth. His hair was wet with sweat and his clothes torn.

"BOB, what happened?"

It was obvious he had been in a fight, but who? Why?

Later he would boast about the event with the unbelievable story of two of Johnny's men who jumped him as he got out of his car.

"They were supposed to kill me, but they each thought the other was going to do the shooting." Bob laughed as he continued to explain, "Johnny tol' you to do it", one said, and then the other said he wasn't told, and he wasn't going to."

We didn't know whether to laugh or be worried.

"Anyway," Bob was laughing hysterically now, "Neither one wanted to kill me, so they just beat the shit out' a me and took off!"

Bob had told me once, he always felt he would be killed, but not like this. He said, "I always believed I would be killed by one of my girls."

Would it be DeeDee, I wondered. Could I do it?

"Oh, my God, Kim!" DeeDee suddenly busted into the living room exclaiming, "I've got to tell you what happened the other night! But," her voice dropped to a whisper "But, you can't tell anyone."

I looked at her with complete and utter shock. She wanted to tell me something in confidence! I wondered if it was a test or a set up to get me in trouble. Since the first time we met, we had not gotten along and now she wants to tell me something and she is trusting me not to tell a sole!

"Everyone was asleep, and I was having this wild dream that I was going to kill Bob"

"Really!" I said surprised.

"And then, I woke… up…standing…over him...with a LOADED pistol aimed right at him!"

"WHAT??! Did he wake up!?" I asked with wide eyes.

"No thank God, but I almost dropped the gun, but I caught it and put it away before he could wake up."

Chapter 19

Greeting the tall perspective trick and his friend, I asked how they were doing.

"Not bad, just out partying" One of them answered. "We just got here and are looking for a good time."

I smiled and looked at Maggie who had been with us for about one month.

"Us, too."

Maggie looked at the two men standing in front of us and played her part.

"Oooo, Kim, he's cute, can I have him?"

I looked back to the men who were now smiling. "How much?" asked the tall blond.

"Well, it depends on what you want. Twenty for head, twenty-five for a straight. Thirty for half and half."

We agreed on thirty for half-and-half and they followed us to the apartment walking about fifteen steps behind us.

After some time, it was obvious that the two tricks had too much to drink to be able to come and it was time to get them out. Unfortunately, they did not agree.

"Look," I reasoned. "It's not your fault, it's just the booze. You've had too much."

Maggie was having the same frustrating problem with her trick and trying to reason with him. Hers was a little more reasonable, but still didn't want to give up.

The situation was quickly escalating to a possible volatile stage, in which I found myself having to be more authoritative and not subservient.

Insistently I told them to get dressed and leave, now. Maggie and I had already dressed, and we would have simply left, except who knows what they would have done to the apartment.

"Yeah?" Jim said in stern defiance, "Gim'me my money back."

"I can't do that," I insisted "we have been here with you for almost an hour." This was a lot longer than any other trick that couldn't come. I must have sensed trouble to allow it to go on this long.

"GIM'ME MY MONEY BACK!" he said through clinched teeth and blazing eyes as his temper rose.

"No" I calmly said as I shook my head and shrugged my shoulders. That is when I noticed that Maggie and her trick had joined us. Maggie looked worried.

More vicious and looking as if he was getting ready to do some damage, my trick got up into my face and in a threatening voice that reminded me of a sound I heard in the pitch-black back woods of Pennsylvania.

"Do you know WHO I AM? Do you KNOW!?" His voice threatening and his body rigid with anger and I knew at that moment he was not someone to go up against. I was thankful for his friend, who jumped in to try to defuse the situation. However, my trick looked like he wasn't used to being told no and was just drunk enough to prove it. I had never been in a position like this with a trick, that I can recall, but I was now and it was a dangerous one.

"Jimmy," he said reaching out for his arm. "Jimmy," he repeated then in a voice of friendship he said, "They don't know who you are, let's go."

However, Jimmy had already passed the point of reason. The alcohol coursing through his veins didn't help to quiet his rage.

I could see in his face, he was giving me one last chance.

"GIM'ME MY MONEY BACK!"

"OKAY, okay," I wondered where my defender of stupidity was. He always claimed to know where we were, and he would be there to protect us should he need to be. I reached into my pocket to pull the money out,

"Okay, here, now leave." I demanded. Inside I was scared shitless, but outside I appeared fearless and indomitable.

His angry dampened but fueled inside with an uncontrolled fever, Jimmy seething said "Now…give me the rest of your money."

"Oh, no you don't" and "Oh, Crap!" simultaneously rushed through my head.

Then I barked back that I didn't have any, Jimmy called my bluff in a rougher tone. "GIM'ME THE REST OF YOUR MONEY!" at this moment, Maggie let out a scream the whole building undoubtedly heard. I turned to see that Jimmy's friend had a hold of Maggie's hair. He quickly let go and I instinctively saw my chance to get out.

I shouted "MAGGIE" and ran right into Jimmy's now swinging fist.

For a moment, I had no sense of those around me. However, I did have the sensation of falling. The movement was all happening in slow motion. I felt weightless yet, I was propelled through the air toward the wooden coffee table that sat in front of the battered couch. My body melded with the toppling table and somehow threw me over the edge of the couch to the end table where I knocked the lamp to the floor, breaking into multiple irreconcilable pieces. I didn't feel the powerful impact or remember any sound that surely must have been. I do, however, remember a quick thought as I flew toward the coffee table of: "Oh, man, that's gonna' hurt."

I was totally oblivious of what caused my weightless tumble, I was only aware of my body's motion and the muted colors that smeared in an ark above me.

As I regained consciousness, I could hear, see, and feel a sound similar to the sound the television makes after the station goes off the air. I felt very off balance because my head was being controlled by this sound. I had a sense of emergency even though I couldn't remember why. As I struggled to get to my feet, I was surprised to find myself in the studio apartment alone.

"Oh, yes," I silently told myself, "I remembered now, Jimmy, his friend, the money he wanted…and… "MAGGIE!"

Just thinking made my head spin harder and I was unable to stand straight up and barely able to open my eyes enough to see where I was going.

I wasn't able to speak yet, though my thoughts seemed clear to me. Because of the quiet in the apartment and the lack of human presents I wondered if I had been out long. I held onto my head to try to stop the spinning and keep myself conscious as I stumbled my way across the room to the open door. As difficult as it was, I tried to look down the hall for the two tricks. The hall was silent as if no one was home, as if hearing the frightening commotion, everyone decided it was time to leave, to deny hearing any sound should the police come later.

The neighboring doors were all shut tight. Not a sound, no music or the rattle of pots and pans preparing supper for the evening, or children shouting to their parents that they didn't want to go to bed. Just silence.

It took all my strength to maintain my footing although my head screamed at me to go back and lay down. It was the urgency I was feeling and the adrenaline pushing through that kept me vertical, albeit at a ninety-degree angle.

"No one there". I told myself.

Again, wondering if I had been out for a long time or just a few minutes, I knew it was more important to find Maggie than to lie down or look at my watch.

I felt like I was going to pass out again. I placed one hand on the wall to stable myself and bent my head down closer to the floor as I shielded my eyes from the light of the hallway. The light felt brighter than the sun itself, forcing my eyes closed and my head down.

"I have to keep going," I told myself "I can't afford the luxury of worrying about only me."

I shook my head in the vain attempt to straighten up, unfortunately, it only made the spinning worse and the light brighter.

By the time I reached the elevator I was feeling like I could stand with a little more assurance, but still quite woozy. I stood for just a short moment to ask myself:

"If I was Maggie, if it was me, where would I go?"

It barely took a millisecond before it came to me. I would not take the elevator, that would take too long. I would go into the trash shoot closet which was to my immediate right provided my pursuers didn't see me. It was worth a chance.

I reached for the heavy door and with all my strength quickly swung it open. There, there, crouched in the corner, in years of unkempt greasy filth from paper bags that tore on the bottom dumping the trash onto the floor or over stuffed bags too large for the shoot, crouched in a small ball of legs, arms, and terror was Maggie. She looked like a frightened child hiding in the corner of her closet after hearing the sound of an enraged intruder. Her arms covering her tangled hair, face streaked from frightened tears and pure terror in her eyes.

She startled and let out a quick scream until she realized it was me. She jumped to her feet, and reached for me, hanging tight as she frantically spewed in a shaky voice,

"Is it safe, yet?"

About an hour too late to rescue us, Bob came home. Seeing us sitting on the couch, he asked why we were not out working. I wasn't in the mood for his anger, but I knew I had to relax my frustration at his tardiness in order to talk to him.

As calmly as I could while still comforting Maggie, I explained what happened. I wanted to ask him where he was, the one that claimed he knew more about us and what we were doing than we did. The one who said he was always around to protect us from bad tricks. Where the hell were you!

His first question was "Did he get the money?" before asking if we got his name.

"Jimmy is what the other guy called him."

"Jimmy? Jimmy what?"

"I don't know" I answered.

We could see the anger in his eyes and the revenge he wanted. However, two days later when I asked if he found them. His answer was a tempered…

"No."

"Do you know who they were?" I asked knowing I was pushing it, but I had to know. I wanted to know just how far he was willing to go to protect us.

Bob hesitated. It was obvious he knew and was afraid.

Then he answered, before changing the subject.

"Yes…"

"Do you know WHO I AM? Do you KNOW!?"

As per usual, Bob never mentioned the situation, Jimmy or Jimmy's friend again. In lieu of everything that happened that night, I knew I did the safest thing when I gave the money back.

His words rolled over and over as I tried to figure out who would be so dangerous that Bob would only want to forget it ever happened.

"Do you know who I am? Do you know who I am?"

Then I asked myself, "The mob? Could Jimmy and his friend be part of the mob? Oh, that's absurd, why would the mob want to pay for sex? They could have any number of mob groupies they wanted, even other mob member's wives, if they really wanted. But, then again, is it possible Jimmy was in the mob?"

It was too much for Maggy and it wasn't long before she ran. Then, not to much longer after Maggy was gone, I decided to run as well. In the past, I had been brought back by force and then whipped. This time would be different though. This time I would not be caught.

It was different because this time, I called Bob so I could come back.

Chapter 20

The hard bump of the airplane wheels on the runway jolted me from a short moment of peace to the realization of where I was and what I was doing coupled with the desperate desire to allow sleep once again to take hold where I could escape the gloom that darkened my world.

The screeching engines whorled to a speed that was more conducive to rubber tires having contact with pavement. Then the high-pitched wail of the reverse engines began to grow in intensity reminding me I was back. I was gone for about four days, but I was once again without a home or means in which to survive. Once again, I felt trapped, unable to survive outside the grip of Bob.

Slowly, the 727 taxied to the predetermined entrance into the terminal where he would be waiting for the run-a-way to return home. There was a sudden halt that forced everyone's body forward just slightly. We are here.

We are here. I am back. Back to "that toddling town" that refers to itself as "The Windy City", where Frank Sinatra sang: "Bet your bottom dollar you lose the blues in Chicago" where my faith and my soul deteriorated more and more each day.

As the engines wound down, the cabin became a flood of conversation and baggage scraping the bottom edge of the overhead bins. Of anxious passengers happy to arrive or stressed about meeting their connecting flight. Men, women, children all trying to be the first one out, all oblivious to the plight that awaits me at the end of the walkway. I wanted to call out for help, but I wouldn't. Soon the voices and mulling about went silent and I felt alone as the last of the passengers walked out the cabin door. Did they notice me, or was I nobody, again like that hooker that died in the hotel room that first week I was in Chicago.

"Excuse me, miss" the young stewardess said. "We have landed. Do you need some help?"

"YES!" I screamed inside.

However, it was "No, thank you." that came out. I reached for my bag wondering if it was too late to change my mind. Could I just stay on the plane and fly out of here? Or, maybe Bob was late or didn't even come to get me.

I slowly left what I felt was the last bit of hope in that airplane and made my way down the enclosed walkway to the man I feared and despised. Entering the terminal, I looked up from the floor and there he stood...alone. The closer I got the bigger his smile was. Many would think it was Daddy welcoming his baby home for the summer but was just a pimp waiting the return of his runaway whore.

"Welcome home, Kim"

"Kim?" I thought, "Kim? Do you even remember my real name?"

It didn't happen often, but now and then Bob would take us all out to party. It was always a welcome diversion from the constant stream of tricks and hoes.

"Get dressed, girls" Bob announce, "We're taking the night off."

He didn't have to tell us twice, it took exactly four minutes and five seconds for the five of us to get dressed and head out the door. Nights off came few and far between and we didn't want Bob to change his mind like he had in the past when we took longer than he wanted.

"He must be in a good mood tonight." Sammy whispered.

"Yeah. Must be" I agreed.

"I just hope it lasts." she whispered.

At that moment, an ominous feeling crept over me. A quick whisper of a warning, it was similar to the feeling you might get while standing on your front porch with a quiet wind rising under a dark sky in the middle of Tornado Alley Kansas. It was as if all the conditions were right that night for a tornado with a vendetta and an agenda of destruction. Although, I had not been back too long, maybe a couple of months, I had not forgotten the periodic warnings I felt. Warnings such as the one I got that resulted in the beating Terry received during a nightly walk with my dog, Pepper. Had I accepted her invitation to tag along, I would have been beat, as well. It was a feeling I always welcomed because it helped me to stay safe, but equally feared because it usually meant something bad was just beyond the next door.

We walked through the heavy front door into the dark player's bar, loud with music from a man hidden from view with a stack of 45's and a turntable. Booths lined the walls. The smell of beer and liquor was a familiar one, and the air heavy with cigarettes and cigars. The benches were made of green vinyl and cracked in spots from years of wear. The bar itself was situated in the middle of the room and tables dotted the floor other than the rather large empty dance floor save two ho's dancing together.

Bob liked to dance, and he would take one of us to the dance floor. I tried to follow his lead, but I had never seen his style of dancing before. It seemed to go best when the blues were playing. With his arms bent and held up high by his armpits, it was somewhat of a swagger with a slow kick and a twist of the hip. Something like you might see from a drunk fish trying to swim in a straight line.

Bob instructed us to sit in a specific booth before he went up to the bar. The booths were quite large and the five of us fit very well with room to spare. DeeDee decided to play the jukebox.

"You watch... it's going to be country" Brenda grunted. "She's a real hillbilly, you know."

DeeDee came from a small village in the heart of Hillbilly-Ville, Kentucky. On a couple of occasions, I had gone with Bob and DeeDee to visit her family. It was interesting to see where and how she grew up. The house was actually sitting over one side of a deep gulch looking down about forty to fifty feet. It had been slowly eroding away over the years making it necessary to brace the rear end with sturdy wooden slats. Her mother was a happy lady but would take no guff from anyone. She seemed spirited and caring and welcomed us all in as if we were all family. She knew about Bob, so thereby knew about the rest of us even though she rarely looked at me speaking only to invite me in. She joked with Bob about learning the country way of "making love."

"Yeah, well, we in the city know how to take care of our ladies."
Bob teased back.
"Ain't no way! No way no city folk kin love like a countryman lovin' his bride," DeeDee's mom retaliated "Until you can git that 'thang' movin' round n' round with nuthin' but pure hip action an' fly on top a yo a 'waitn' true love from across th' room, you ain't ne'er come close to espar-encin' true country lovin'."

As predicted, DeeDee put on an old country song by Loretta Lynn, "You Ain't Woman Enough to Take My Man"
"Yup, you pegged her," Sue laughed as she complimented Brenda on her keen sense.
It wasn't too difficult, though, DeeDee never listened to anything other than country music.
When DeeDee rejoined us, our drinks were already on the table being enjoyed by the rest of us. We sat and chitchatted about nothing in particular, when a man who was obviously too drunk for his own good, came up to the table to introduce himself.

"Par' don-a mua, ladies," he slurred "My name is Phillip Scandella, and I would like to invite you over to my table for a few drinks."

His first request was politely refused, however, he would return to our table another three times. Each time he returned to renew his invitation, he was a little more drunk and we were a little less polite.

"Ladies," he slurred "May I be so bored, I mean, barred, um," He took a deep breath and tried again. "May I so, be so b,b,BOLD as ask your pres..."

DeeDee cut him off at this point and barked "Look, we are here just trying to have a nice time. We are NOT going to party with the likes of you! GO AWAY and don't come back!"

"Well..." Phillip's attempted at being a gentleman was dashed only because of his balance and intoxication. "I TIP my HAT and say, adieu ladies." he reached for his absent hat, feeling his balding head in case he just missed it, did it fall off his head? Looking around the floor. Nope, must a' left it at the table.

He took a formal bow and returned to his table.

DeeDee had had enough. It was time to go to Bob for help.

"He'll get rid of him." DeeDee relayed with conviction as she went to find him.

We were all losing our humor.

"That idiot is a real jerk" Heidi growled.

"Ya, but Bobby will get rid of him." I said to Heidi.

"I know," she replied with the same growl and squinty eyes of hatred.

When DeeDee returned to the table she asked if he had come back again, to which we said no. She then told us that Bob would be over soon and had an idea.

We all sat in our seats fuming as we wondered if Bob would come before the "jackass" returned. Those few moments seemed to take forever, but eventually Bob came. Leaning into us avoiding noisy looky-loos,' he handed DeeDee a pistol. He began whispering instructions as he continued handing out pistols to each of us. I wondered at first if he actually had that many, however, I believe he only carried one pistol which was always tucked neatly under the back of his blazer. I suspect he went to his pimp friends and borrowed their pistols to pull off the ruse.

When we each had our pistol sitting in our laps, he simply turned and left us to take care of his business while keeping a watchful eye on what was to happen. I felt a bit nervous as I prepared myself for the phony threat. The others may have been willing to follow through with the threat and DeeDee certainly would, but I did not intend to shoot this defenseless idiot.

"Here he comes, here he comes." DeeDee whispered. "Act normal and do this calmly."

As he leaned in and opened his mouth once more to tempt us with his drunkenness, the five of us placed a pistol on the table in front of our self. We didn't even acknowledge his presents but remained calm. The message was loud and clear and Ol' Phillip straightened himself up and

raised his hands in submissive surrender as he back away from us without a word.

Bob returned to retrieve the pistols, he was laughing about the whole scene as he told us we were going to be leaving and to get ready while he returned the guns to their owners. So, as we finished our drinks we were laughing and talking about the antics with Ol' Phillip.

Bob joined us as we stood up to leave, "That drunk, what was his name?" Bob asked,

"Ol' Phillip," which prompted even more laughter.

"Yeah," Bob continued as we left, "Ol' Phillip, tell me again what happened when you all laid your pistols out on the table."

We were still laughing and talking as we were driving home for the night. It was in the middle of our ride when Sue decided to bring up something I assume had been on her mind.

"Bobby?"

At first, nobody thought about it until she went on. "You are a great man, and I know you're fair and good to us."

I wondered what she was getting at.

She continued "So I know when I ask you, you will continue showing the respect that you have always shown me." By this time, everyone in the car had gotten a little quieter.

"Bobby?" She asked with total innocents and a death-wish sense of confidence in this egotistical, masochistic deviant, poor excuse for a man who has not had a sincere thought for anyone other than satisfying his own flesh and ego,

"Bobby, Will you sell me to a black pimp."

Chapter 21

Bob had mentioned to me many times in the last couple of years
how difficult it was to be white in a black man's world. He was
constantly being challenged, threatened, and laughed at. He had told
me about a time he was driving his car, the window was down, and he
was just cruising down the road when all of a sudden, he was cut off
and forced to stop. The black pimp Bob made a fool out of for having a
stutter, had jumped out of the car and brandished a weapon with a bead
on Bobby. He must have decided it was time for this "white boy" to go
down.

The "would be assailant" quickly showed himself at the driver's
side window where Bob sat busily formulating an escape plan and
route. He knew what the man wanted, and it was obvious if he was
going to get out of this situation alive, he would have to think quick and
act even faster. He quickly scanned the area for his escape route while
stalling for time.

"The doors are locked," Bob thought, "I have to unlock them
without him realizing then open the door, pushing him off balance, duck
out of the way and race up onto the sidewalk around his car then down
the street taking the first turn I can to get away."

"Yu, yu, you a d-dead man!" He shoved his pistol toward Bob's
open window.

"MAAAN," Bob whined "What you want to do me like this for?"

"C-cuz, you d-disre-s-spected me in front of my-my ladies." He spat out vile profanity as Bob continued trying to talk his way out. Then raising his hand up Bob loudly spouted "DAMN, ya' got me." at the exact same time bringing his fists down on the door lock to appear as if he was disgusted in himself for being in the wrong place at the wrong time. When Bob hit the lock with his fist as he shouted, he was essentially covering up the ca' lack of the electric lock, unlocking the door. He then pushed the door open and into his assailant throwing him off balance and knocking him down onto the pavement. In that same instant, Bob threw the shift into drive, slammed the accelerator to the floor and sped off with his head ducked down to avoid the gunfire from the irate pimp.

Sue went on to explain that Bobby was a great pimp but that she simply felt more comfortable with a black pimp.

"You can understand, can't you Bobby?" She said with a pause.

I leaned up and whispered that she needed to shut up before something happened.

However, Sue wouldn't have it. "No, KEE-IMMM," She said in the same way a child would when he or she would be trying to get someone else in trouble. "I won't shut up." She wanted to be sure Bob, as well as the others in the car, heard that I was trying to stop her.

Sue continued her damning chatter with no more than a hairline pause.

"You're really good, and the girls are really great. They all get along and I will miss you all, I'm just used to a black pimp and feel more comfortable with a black pimp rather than a white one."

Blah, blah, blah, here's a shovel to dig your grave a little deeper. Would you like your funeral with or without last rights?

I could see the anger building on Bob's face even though he appeared as if he had not heard a word she said. However, I can tell you that he was listening to every syllable out of the girl's mouth. It was obvious by the tension in his knuckles as he gripped the wheel tighter and tighter. There was a subtle tensing of his jaw and the muscles in his neck. He was driving faster, barely noticing the other cars or people we passed. He didn't even slow down enough to round the corners safely because I remember the whining as we squealed around the corner of our street. Sue began to wonder what was going on, but it didn't deter her, much, from continuing with her desire for the quality Bob could not add to his arsenal of pimp-hood, changing his race to black.

"Shut...up...Sue" I tried once more with a quiet voice even though I knew everyone in the car could hear, I only hoped my warnings would not prompt a blow from the raging thunder that was coming closer and closer with each word from Sue's mouth.

As we raced closer to the apartment, we could hear and smell the laboring engine being pushed beyond its limit. Bob's knuckles were tightly wrapped on the wheel that even the high pressure of his blood could not find a clear path to the tips of his fingers and I feared for Sue and what Bob would do when he unleashed this murderous rage. His forearms were tensing, and his jaw line was now flexing from gritting his teeth with the building wrath. Never had I ever witnessed such evil holding a body captive.

"So? Bobby?" She said completely oblivious to the venom she was mixing through her blasphemous words. "Do you think you could? I mean, sell me? Any pimp will do. As long as he is black."

"As long as he is black...black...black"

Each block flashed past with a fury of colors and lights, Bob's expression showed little emotion except to those who had learned the signs. We knew his rage, I had never witnessed or experienced it to this magnitude before, but I knew the evil that could be unleashed, if provoked enough. The woman that accused him of attempted murder knows, DeeDee knows and soon everyone in the car would know.

I could see the next turn coming up as everyone braced their self to stay upright. Then rounding the corner, I could feel the force of my weight being pulled against Sammy and the shrill scream of the tires against the concrete as they threatened to go airborne. I was afraid of what would happen if anyone dared to ask him to slow down and I prayed no one especially Sue, would open their mouth.

I watched DeeDee as she fought to keep her center position in the front seat and not collide into either Bob or Sue. She stared straight ahead unmoving, I'm not sure if it was in response to the frenzied drive home or fear of the madman at the wheel.

We continued racing down the street passing two-flats and parked cars, yet Bob did not appear to even notice. As we neared the apartment, I felt a rush of relief finally to be coming to a stop, but terrified of what was to come next.

Bob hit the brakes with the force of a jet plane flying full throttle into a freestanding brick wall. The putrid odor of burning rubber, asphalt, and an overheated engine permeated the air, but no attention was paid. The radiator spewing anti-freeze and water up under the hood then onto the street went disregarded. The only thoughts of our party, save Bob, was to get out of the car, stay as clear of Bob as possible and to follow the explicit orders from the maniac who was out for blood. Even one demand not followed in a nano-second could result in a duplicate beating.

The first demand came in a low-leveled growl ordering DeeDee to. "Get...that...bitch...in...the...house."

We wasted no time getting in the front door of the two flat.

We could all feel it, this was going to be bad. Not one sound came from anyone, except for Sue who ignorantly asked "What's going on? What's going on? Why did we have to hurry?"

DeeDee had it with Sue. "Will you just stop talking!"

Bob came up the walk, in strides of conviction. His face now opened in fury as he paced up and down the walkway. With his arms straight along his sides, each carrying the same clinched knuckles that held around the steering wheel was now balled into fists. The same mouth that only a short time ago was happy and laughing was now tightly clinching an angry frown. His eyes narrowed as they sought out the "disrespectful, canker sore on the ass of a maggot bitch."

Everyone stood around the living room as if we were encircling a fighting ring between a hungry lion and an oblivious butterfly. All close enough to snap to orders yet far enough to escape any misguided swing. Bob closed the front door

"Shut the curtains" he demanded in a monotone voice as he made his way to the center of the ring. We all jumped as if a rattlesnake crawled out from the floorboards but DeeDee was closest to the window and was able to reach it the fastest.

The room was silent except for the whishing sound of hooks being drawn over a one dollar and ninety-nine cents, dime store curtain rod, the outside lights no longer penetrated the window and the bitter taste of the impending assault was hidden from the nosy and the busybodies.

Bob walked past Sue without even looking at her, but quickly turned as he growled at her foolishness.

"You should have listened to Kim." then striking Sue with such a blow she was knocked off her feet and would have fallen into Sammy had she not taken a short hop back. Sue had barely realized what happened as she was looking back to her attacker when, with the growl of a pouncing lion, he threw himself over her, straddling her body and delivered another blow to her jaw. He was viciously shouting insults and profanity at her with an uncontrolled fury, striking her over and over as she vainly tried to shield her face.

The rest of us helplessly watched in horror, as this madman attacked her without mercy. I felt like a child watching as a bear mauling another child. Afraid to jump in for fear that the bear will strike me with his mighty claw and having nowhere to turn to find help for the child being mauled to death. I felt myself covering first my head then my face, turning my head to see the others as they were responding in similar reactions of fear and shock. We had all felt the arm of his wrath before and we all wanted desperately for it to stop. We feared for ourselves and the foolish girl enduring the assault alone in a room full of people.

Bob continued beating her as her face began to bleed. The piercing of her skin came by the sheer force of his blows as well as the diamonds in his rings, paid for by the group of us watching and the one he was pummeling. Empathetically, I felt each blow and each sting from each diamond as it tore into her flesh. Bob stood up breathing heavily, fists bloody and still rolled into tight balls. The muscles in his forearms hardened and transformed into long bulging tendons that screamed to be released, to be free to again ravish more hatred on the young teenager.

"CLEAN HER UP!" he demanded as he began to walk away.

We all leapt to Sue's aid, but it was short lived. We heard the roar of thunder as he reeled back around wielding both fists lifted high above his head prompting the rest of us to quickly move away. He pounced on her sending the rest of us jumping backward away from the attack. He came down on her like a great ape throwing his massive arms down in anger. He shouted and bellowed more insults on top of insults coupled with foul profanity that covered her person like blackened ooze.

He then grabbed Sue by the front of her blouse, heaved her to the other side of himself, and pummeled her with more blows to her chest and head. Releasing her from his grip, he again ordered us to clean her up. This time Bob walked to the back bedroom, giving us enough time to walk her just into the hallway before he again unleashed yet another attack.

With both fists, he enveloped her in a barrage of punches that both shocked and mortified us. I saw a couple of the girls holding tears back and another who had turned her face away from this horrific act. With each rapidly placed blow, his words raised in intensity. He was standing over her as she was pinned on the floor between the wall and his blows.

She was crying apologies intermingled with cries for him to stop. I heard gasps from the shock of witnessing Sue's body repeatedly knocking and bouncing against the wall by the force and repetition of his jackhammer punching.

It was only when he was totally exhausted and Sue was nearly unconscious that he stood up, chest heaving with each labored breath, that he stopped his attack and stormed off down the hallway ordering us to clean her up.

We surrounded her with words of sympathy and acts of kindness. Jessica ran for a cool washcloth to gently clean her wounds and dab her tears. Then we heard it, again.

"DeeDee, get that BITCH IN HERE!" it was heard loud and clear from the bedroom where Bob had gone just a few moments earlier.

Sue's eyes widened, her arms pushing against us and cries of terror, pleading with us to not make her go.

"Please," she cried, "Please, don't make me go." We could hear the panic in her voice. We had no choice, we had to comply, and if we did anything else Bob would become more enraged and not only would he jump on us for not doing as he said but it would be much worse for Sue. We didn't know what we could do to comfort her when there was no comfort to be had.

I wanted to provide support for her but then I felt like I would be walking her down that long green hall to her execution. I couldn't stop the beating and I was useless for comfort.

We offered up apologies that would not be of any help.

"It should be okay" Someone said.

"I don't think he'll do anymore." Came from another.

"Please, please, please" begged Sue with bloody arms reaching out for a sanctuary that was unable to come. "Don't make me go in there, please, please, don't make me." However, we didn't have a choice. DeeDee gently helped her up from the floor and put her arm around her weakened body, helping her to where Bob waited. Tears flowed and pleads for sympathy and more cries not to make her go went all the way down the hall. Sue was hardly able to stand as DeeDee guided her steps.

She was whispering something to Sue, and I wondered what form of condolences could possibly be offered as she was led trembling into the pit of evil. DeeDee cautiously opened the bedroom door and gently pushed Sue in before slowly closing the door behind her and returning to help us clean the blood from the carpet and wall.

A few minutes went by quietly. A welcomed sound and no one broke the silence as we feverishly worked with dish soap, baking soda, and anything else we could think of to clean up the massive amount of blood. Then we heard it, a sudden high-pitched scream pierced the quiet and our hearts leapt high. "It's started again!" Someone warned. "Was that Sue!!?" another person asked as we all looked at each other, questioning.

"KIM!" It was Bob

I jumped up as I shouted to myself "SHIT!"

I ran down the hall as fast as I could and threw open the door. Sue was on the floor between the wall and the bed holding her hand up in defense of more blows as she was crying "I'm sorry, I'm sorry, I didn't mean it, I'm sorry."

Bob stood, his pants down around his ankles and his penis bloody

"SHE BIT MY DICK OFF, SHE BIT MY DICK OFF. I was hitting her on both side of her head, but she wouldn't let go! She just wouldn't let go!!! She bit my dick off!!!

I couldn't see just how bad she had bitten him, there was so much blood all over him, his hands, and Sue's mouth. I thought she might have cut him bad with her teeth until he told DeeDee to find the missing piece of his manhood. Through torrents of apologetic tears, arms up in defense and cries of not meaning to, Sue pointed to the spot she had spit out the wretched piece of bloody flesh. DeeDee quickly retrieved it with a wad of toilet paper and carried it all the way to the emergency room where the doctor on call would re-attach it.

Chapter 22

We were told to watch Sue and under no uncertain terms not to let her run before she healed. Not surprising, it was the first trick she went on that she never returned.

Sammy introduced her brother Matthew, Cal, a friend, and her dog, Jack

"Bobby said we could use your shower?" Sammy spoke as if she had been our neighbor for the last few years.

I smiled in response, but I wasn't really listening to what she said. I was wondering where she had been and why she was calling herself Sammy. I then realized that I was staring at her as she waited for my answer.

"I'm sorry," I heard coming out of my mouth, "What did you ask?"

"I asked where the shower was." she repeated.

I pointed her in the right direction and watched in silence as she began digging through her backpack. I wondered why she needed those things in that grungy bag, surely, we had things in her size.

"Why did I think about that?" I asked myself. With no answer, I dismissed my thoughts as being nothing.

While Sammy continued pulling items out of her backpack, Matt and Cal began telling us their story. The three of them had been hitch hiking across the country to get jobs they had heard about in California.

It made me think of a movie I had seen about the depression and the great migration to California for promised work.

They had little to speak of, only what they could carry on their backs and a piece of beef jerky they must have carried for emergencies. Sammy pulled her prize from her well-traveled jean pocket and I noticed it had some dirt and strands of lint stuck to it. She smiled and quickly brushed it off with her just as dirty hands. I wondered why it wasn't wrapped in something like a sandwich bag or a napkin, even a tissue or piece of toilet paper from a gas station restroom would be better than nothing at all. I didn't ask, it was none of my business.

With no money for food or rooms, they depended on the generosity of those they ran into. When Megan asked where they slept at night, Sammy proudly said they had camping gear in their backpacks.

At first, Sammy was just another girl Bobby was trying to pull. I assumed she would be coerced into staying with the promise of food, money and California. Those very things she wanted most of all. She appeared to be quite adventurous in nature and proud of where she came from. She called it "old money"

"Our parents are rich, and I grew up with servants." she explained.

Other than her words, she appeared to be a little lacking in the self-confidence area, if that is possible with the silver spoon she possessed.

It would only take a day for Bob to run the boys off, leaving Sammy and her dog behind. There didn't seem to be any issues with Sammy staying while the others went on. I never heard, and I never asked.

Although I felt a bit uneasy about Sammy's motives for staying, I welcomed her, to our clan in the way only I could do and get away with.

As I headed out to meet a trick of mine, I saw Sammy by the door.

"Hey, would you do me a favor?" I asked.

I didn't want the others to spoil my prank, so I asked Sammy to follow me. When we got out to my car, I asked her to hold my spot. Our apartment had street parking only, it was difficult sometimes to find a close spot to park, and I had a prime spot, right in front of our building.

It was also common to find those construction cones blocking prime parking spots.

"Why don't you use some of those cones?"

My answer sufficed and she stood in my parking spot as I drove off down the street and turned the corner.

Later, after I returned, she said she waited about fifteen minutes before deciding I wasn't coming back.

Sammy had been a member of our group for only a short time before I recognized her, and it was in that moment that I saw she wasn't who she was claiming to be. Bobby had brought her to the apartment and introduced her as "Sammy". However, I knew, oh yes I knew it was all a big ruse

"There must be a reason!" I discretely told myself as we sat in a restaurant eating breakfast. Bobby might hear me if I'm not careful and I wouldn't want him to know that I recognized her, not yet anyway. So, with every thought, I bit my lower lip so I wouldn't say anything out loud. Trying to be inconspicuous, I kept watch on her throughout our meal, trying to figure out, why.

"Yes, I can see it now." Sammy was not who she was claiming to be, and it only took a moment for me to see who she was. She was…Maria. But why, why was she concealing her identity from us, no, from me!

Maria was the only real friend I had since Carmen was sold and was sent back to Cleveland. She came to us at a time I needed a friend the most. I felt comfortable with Maria, we shared some wonderful conversations together and soon, shared secrets we did not feel we could tell anyone else. Together, we felt confident enough to withstand most anything that would come our way, and we could comfort each other when Bobby would find a reason to beat one of us. We even became blood sisters.

Maria was first to prick her finger with a knife. It took only a second for her wound to begin to bleed. I was a little more skittish than she was, I worried it would hurt.

"Go ahead Kim.." She encouraged, "it doesn't hurt much."

One of the hardest moments I ever spent was when I was told Maria was sold away, and I was told I would never be able to see her again. Bob said it was what she wanted. That hurt.

Was my best friend incognito because she is afraid? Was she sent by the police under a new identity to spy on us, Bob - *me*? Why wasn't I told by someone, anyone? I just didn't know. What I did know was Sammy was not who she was claiming to be, and everyone was trying to hide it from me.

As we left the restaurant, I stayed back with Megan and Bob as the others went up ahead laughing and talking. I wanted to let Bob know that I knew Sammy was Maria anonymously but I didn't want to blurt it out. I leaned in close to Bob as I kept my eye on Maria.

"Are you sure…she's not Maria?" I asked to show him that I knew.

Bob stopped and leaned back to get a better look at me and in an "I don't believe what I am hearing." tone, Bob asked "WHO!?"

I turned my head in the direction of the girls, then, I turned my gaze on Bob without adjusting the direction of my head I whispered "Sammy."

In utter disbelief, Bob insistently said "Yes, I'm sure!" Then just as quick he asked, "Are you alright?!"

Turning to face straight ahead, I decided it was better to forget the whole conversation I had with Bob. "Uh, yeah, yeah, I mean, of course I'm okay." I told him I was fine and "No problem here…just forget that little misunderstanding." Pretending I hadn't said a word out of the ordinary. I turned away but he kept looking at me as we began walking to the car. He didn't say another word, but I knew now, oh, yes I did, I knew now that he was in on the deception, as well. They were all trying to keep me from knowing that Maria was back and calling herself…Sammy..

It was the following morning, Bob came in as he usually did to collect the money we had made from the night before. This morning, however, was a little different, this time he announced that we were going to visit his parents in Crystal Lake. I wasn't sure how I felt about going to meet my pimp's parents.

As we approached the front door, I became worried about what they would say with all of us coming at one time. However, Bob assured me that his parents were wonderful people who accepted everyone he brought home.

"But do they know?" I asked, not sure what answer I was hoping to get. "I mean, do they know about us?"

Bob answered with confidence, "I never told them, but I think they know. And Kim, don't worry, they will love you."

I never did find out if they knew their son was a pimp or not, for sure, because as Bob said, they were both wonderful people who appeared very obliging and accepting of us all.

Crystal Lake was a nice neighborhood of neatly trimmed lawns, sunny porches with porch swings and metal porch chairs painted white so as not to clash with the color of the house. Flowers surrounded the homes and about every home had mature shade trees in the front and back yards. Crystal Lake was nothing like the neighborhood I lived and worked in, it was…quiet. It always felt like the dark clouds of the city were lifted to allow the sun to shine, even when it was raining, it felt calming.

I was pleased with the way Bob's parents acted toward all of us. I thought about what I may feel if the tables were turned and I had a son who was a pimp. I wasn't sure if I could be as congenial as Bob's folks were. They welcomed us as if we were friends from just down the street invited over for a few drinks and an exciting game of Bridge or Canasta.

As we were getting ready to sit down to dinner, Bob's mother was slicing homemade cheesecake at the counter. Bob came up behind her and gave her a big hug from behind, then began to gag. He stepped back as he continued gagging.

"Are you sure that cheesecake is okay?" he asked between gags.

A bit insulted, tootsie remarked, "Yes! I'm sure, I made it just this afternoon!".

Bob wasn't sure though because his weak stomach gagging was telling him different. We all gathered around smelling the cheesecake to see if it was bad when tootsie looked down to see Sammy's dog, who had joined us on our visit.

"It has to be the dog!" She insisted, but Bob wouldn't accept the idea that what he was smelling was the dog.

"It's fine!" She insisted, "Now let's all sit down and eat before I decide to throw it in your face!"

Through dinner nothing much was mentioned whether the cheesecake was truly tainted or not and we all thoroughly enjoyed the tender pot roast, potatoes, carrots and rolls. Bob demonstrated his satisfaction by leaning to his right side a little and released a particularly loud fart just as Sammy's dog passed behind and gagged. It may have been divine sense of humor or simple coincidence, whichever it was, there was a lot of dopamine released that evening.

After the dishes were cleaned and a little more visiting completed, it was time to head back to the city. Bob came to me and told me that I was going to stay for a couple of days.

"Days?! Why?" I was surprised and not very sure I liked the idea. "Are you going to stay, too?"

He told me he had to go back to the city to take care of business but assured me he would be back and that he would call me.

"But why do I have to stay?" I pushed, "Why can't I go back with you?"

Very gently, Bob told me that I had not been feeling well lately and that I needed to rest. Tootsie, Bob's mother and a registered nurse, was standing close by. I wondered what was going on. I felt fine, I hadn't been complaining of feeling ill.

Bob eventually put his foot down, "Kim, I want you to stay here for a few days until you feel better."

I didn't quite understand what he meant, I wasn't sick, and I didn't want to stay with Bob's parents, not now. I pleaded with him not to make me stay, but was told I had to stay, at least for a few days.

The first few days were a blur, I was to stay in bed getting up only to go to the bathroom. tootsie gave me coffee, juice, water, in that order every day on timed intervals. She would sit and watch me as I drank the juice.

"You need to drink it all."

I didn't argue. I didn't want to drink it all at once, but I didn't want to argue, either.

So, I drank it…every day at three in the afternoon.

Chapter 23

I looked at the clock beside my bed, 1:12. It's dark, it was the middle of the night.

"They should be sleeping by now." I told myself.

I hated sitting in that room, day in, day out. The same view when I wake up, as when I fall asleep. No television, no radio and…no telephone. I think that one bothered me the most because I couldn't even call Bob to see what was happening or how things were going. To touch the city just a little bit.

I looked at the clock again, "1:18, they're surely asleep." I thought. "Maybe I could sneak a call."

Quietly I slipped down to the floor. I tried to bury myself into the fibers of the carpet so it would be harder to spot me. I crept across the carpet cautiously listening for any sound to alert me to jump back into the bed covering myself and pretending to sleep.

No sound. It seemed that the telephone was so far away. Intellectually, I knew it was only about ten feet from the bed I had spent so much time in, but my movement was so carefully done that it felt as if it would take me an hour to reach it.

Breathing, I didn't want to breathe too loud. I couldn't hold my breath that long, but I did manage to breathe quiet by keeping each breath shallow.

Reaching the door to my room, I warily checked to see if anyone was in the kitchen looking for a mid-night snack. No soft yellow glow from the refrigerator, no pale light from the kitchen at all other than the moon as it blushed just enough to break up the darkness.

I looked down past the kitchen, now toward the den that had been made into a bedroom some time ago. Even the moons glow didn't reach into their bedroom. They must be asleep otherwise I would think some light would flow from the room. Because I didn't want them to wake up and catch me out of bed, I reached for the green desk telephone not permitting my knees to cross into the hall. Pulling the phone toward me, I hit a snag. The cord wasn't going to reach my bed, it must have only been about three feet stem to stern. Without the ability to make the call from under the covers in my bed, I would have to make it quick.

The tone that came through the receiver seemed so loud, I was sure they could hear, then each time I pushed a number the sound seemed even louder and it resonated against the walls. Now, I was positive it would send the tones right down the hall, through the kitchen and into their bedroom, waking the two of them. Common sense told me, it was impossible, but how do I know how good their hearing is. Bob's father had hearing aids, but it is possible he wore them to throw me off. I needed to talk to Bob, I just had to. I needed to tell him I was feeling good and to come pick me up…now!

Bob had his own apartment and his own phone. It was the only way I could get a hold of him, I hoped he was home.

"Bob?" I whispered into the phone.

"Kim? What's wrong?"

I told him I wanted him to come pick me up.

"I'm okay, I feel fine, please come get me." I pleaded.

It would be a few more days before they all felt I was well enough to go back to the city. I was so happy when he showed up one morning to take me back.

"Are you ready to come home?" he asked.

"Yes, yes, yes" and I ran to throw my things into a grocery back and was back within thirty seconds. I didn't want Bob to change his mind and leave like he did once before.

Bob was especially talkative once we were in the car. He was telling me everything that had gone on since I've been away. There was a new girl by the name of Shelly. She was heavy, but "some tricks like a girl with a little meat on them" he mused. DeeDee was off visiting her family…again.

"It took many, many years of thinking about that whole ordeal that I wondered if Maria had become another faceless, 'just a hooker, no big deal' found murdered and dumped somewhere without respect or regard, and was it at Bob's hand. I still wonder now and then."

I really dreaded those time DeeDee was gone because it always put me in the position of head-ho, and Bob's lackey, so to speak. It was as if he would hinge me to his hip. I was expected to turn tricks and be at his "beck and call". I did not like the idea of spending that much time dealing with his temperament. That was DeeDee's job, not mine.

I believe it was her way of running away legal-like. She wanted out as bad as any one of us did, but she was cemented in. Bob had mixed the powder and added the rock himself. He had married DeeDee which not only protected him from her testifying against him in the attempted murder case, but it tied her closer. He knew her family and he knew where they lived. He also knew that the threat to their safety was enough to cure the cement.

It worked, she always came back.

I didn't care that DeeDee was gone this time, I didn't even care that Bob didn't know when she would return. I was happy I was going back to the city.

Karly and Becky were a couple of girls Bob pulled before DeeDee left. I knew about them, hadn't met them, but Bob had told me about them.

"Karly and Becky ran off," He paused a short second then said, "But that's okay."

I hadn't said much of anything up to that point, he was talking enough for the both of us. But he waited to see if I would say anything this time.

"They sure didn't stay long." I quietly commented.

"Naw," he returned, "Some don't."

"Oh", another pause as he considered what words to use. "And Sammy, you remember Sammy?" He sat looking straight ahead at the road, he seemed almost frozen in his seat. I looked over to him as he drove. He had both hand on the steering wheel. They weren't tense like his hands usually are, but they were, I guess you could say, relaxed, but unmoving. He kept his eyes on the road, not deviating even a little. His profile was very defined and I could see the scenery behind him through the window as a racing blur. I watched his unique, almost perfect profile as I thought about his question. "Do you remember Sammy?"

"Kim, Bob's on the phone for you." I had heard the phone ring and tootsie answer the phone using her last name. I had never heard anyone answer the telephone that way before, it was always "Hello?" When I was growing up I was always told not to give my name before I knew who it was. But Bob's folks regularly answered their phone this way.

I was so excited it was Bob "Is he coming to get me?" tootsie smiled but shrugged to indicate she didn't know.

"Hi, Kim, someone here wants to talk to you." He said.

It was Sammy and I wondered why she wanted to talk to me. I didn't hardly know her.

She took the phone and in a voice you might use when you were talking to a toddler or someone in the Looney Bin, she sung "Hiiii, Kiiiimm. This is...Saaaaaammy", I thought she was nuts. "Yeeesss?" I answered mimicking her musical tune. "Re-meeem..berrr, meee?"

"Yeah," I answered. It was at that point I noticed a slight movement in his shoulders as though he there was a sense of relief. "She's that girl you pulled just before I went to tootsie and Frank's." but it was all I remembered.

The memory of what happened was gone. I had checked out, went looking for Toto, out to lunch, I took a vacation to the land of absence. I had a sudden break from reality brought on by severe depression. I have no idea of how long I was gone, even to this day I don't remember. It would take twenty-some odd years to begin remembering parts of what happened, and I still don't remember much, just what I have told you.

Looking for the familiar, I was surprised to find everything so different. They had moved from the second story apartment into a two-flat on Addison. It had two-bedrooms with one bathroom, a large living room opening to an equally large dining room with a built-in china cabinet. It felt like a real home rather than the hole in the wall dumpsters we had lived in up to that point. I had never seen such a large apartment!

As I looked around, taking in all the unfamiliar setting I saw that the furniture appeared new, cheaply made, but new and the whole place was clean, except for the little bit of kitchen that was visible from where I stood. It felt dark. The light was on, but there was a dark and gloomy feel to it, which made me shudder with a sickening familiarity. The filth and older appliances brought memories of Dearborn Street, Clark Street, LaSalle Street, and that horrible apartment where Bob almost killed Sue when he beat her so badly. That feeling forced me to turn away shutting my eyes very tight as I did my best to push that panic from my mind. I told myself the kitchen was off limits. I never wanted to go in there. I was glad no one noticed the anxiety I experienced. I didn't want to be ushered right back to Crystal Lake.

I noticed the desk in the living room and a Juke box. Bob was talking to Rebecca at that time, who was sitting at the desk. She handed him a small stack of envelopes and some neatly stacked bills.

Rebecca had a spiral notebook, just like the one I gave Bob that morning at breakfast, I wondered what it was all about. Bob was standing next to Rebecca while she sat at the desk pointing at the notebook. I couldn't hear what they were talking about, but it was something Bob approved of as was evident by his bobbing head throughout the conversation. When she had finished and looked up to Bob, he opened each envelope, one at a time then back to the notebook.

When they finished, Bob called the girls and as he handed the envelopes out, he proudly said, "No more streets, Kim, no hotels, or even bars. I had all the girls start collecting names and numbers and now you work only out of the apartment.", which also meant, if we kept to the regulars, no more getting busted. Bob was allowing the girls to keep some of the money, it brought, little as it was, a sense of freedom. It would take me a while to feel totally back to normal and back on track.

Since I had been in respite care, Bob had decided to allow each girl to have a percent of the money she earned. The money was split 60/40 in Bob's favor, of course. Each girl was required to pay $25.00 per day rent and $5.00 for food out of her forty percent. If the girl got more than $10.00 at the end of the workday, she was lucky.

It was at that time I decided, it was time to bring my plan to completion, the plan that would free me forever.

Chapter 24

Bob burst in the apartment with a huge grin.

"Yawl come see the new car",

He bought many new cars during that time, all for cash, all large.
This time was a little different, this time it was a 1972 Eldorado. It was
a beautiful car, black
leather interior, black
outside, a chrome comb
just behind the door and
a flying lady on the
hood.

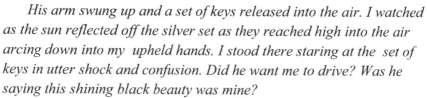

We were all ogling
the shiny symbol of
success when Bob called
out to me. Because of
the tone in his voice, I quickly turned around.

His arm swung up and a set of keys released into the air. I watched
as the sun reflected off the silver set as they reached high into the air
arcing down into my upheld hands. I stood there staring at the set of
keys in utter shock and confusion. Did he want me to drive? Was he
saying this shining black beauty was mine?

I was completely dumbfounded, I looked up to see Bob laughing,
"Aren't you gonna' drive it? It's for you, girl. It's yours!"

Even though Bob had bought a car for DeeDee a while back, it was very apparent that this gift to me truly upset her. It might have been because the car was not the first extravagant gift I received. I had also received a full-length Sable fur coat and a diamond ring, albeit you needed a magnifying glass to see the diamond, it was a diamond ring, nonetheless. Each gift came with it a dead pan look from DeeDee. It didn't bother me, though, because what it told me was my planning was working and he was trusting me and believing I loved him. He had no idea he was slowly handing me what I needed to escape.

It would be a few months before Bob would tell us that the court date had been set and this time he had to go to California. I knew then the time was right, but there were a few things I still had to do. It had taken an entire year of conning the con and now I needed to keep it alive and well.

DeeDee had returned from her visit home a few weeks earlier. It wasn't mentioned whether or not the timing of her return had anything to do with going to go to court with Bob. In fact, she always seemed quite indifferent about the possibility of her husband going to prison for attempted murder. Maybe, she secretly hoped he would go, or maybe she was told never to say a word, whatever the reason she had nothing to do with what I was doing.

"Bob, can I go?" I asked.

"No, not this time." he said with a look I'm not sure I ever saw. It almost seemed like a sincere look of "serious like". Not love, but as if he genuinely cared about me.

I hung my head and with his arms wrapped around me I quietly said, "okay". I'm not sure why, but this time it was difficult to look disappointed. It was just about a year ago that I had stepped into a roll of devoted ho that I had to live if it was to be convincing. My goal was to gain his utmost trust, I never wanted him to begin to really like me as a person, but I think that is what was happening.

"Can't I go?" I would ask a number of times even up to him getting on the airplane.

"No, Kim." He said once more before promising to call me. Then he said, "I have to do this without you. I wish you could go, but you have to stay."

And stay I did, until a phone call set me free.

I put my sewing supplies back in the small basket beside my chair. Looking to my sleeping husband, I said, "I have more stories. Many more, but maybe they are for another time." I took the remote from his lap and turned the television off kissed his bald forehead and went to bed.

I was jolted awake by the familiar voice, the voice I feared for many years, "Kim, get up!"

I opened my eyes to find Bob standing over the bed. My heart leapt in my chest and pounded the familiar tune as I stared in shock.

"But," I managed to spit out. "I'm married, I have children!"

Bob let out a laugh then leaned down to me saying, "You were dreaming! Now, get up and go to work!"

Covering my head with my blanket as if to shield this horrible image from my eyes, I screamed, "No, No, No!" when suddenly I opened my eyes to see the darkness that filled my room. I turned to see where I was…a dream, it was just a dream.

I cozied up to my husband who was now sound asleep. He must have come to been after I fell asleep. I thought to myself as I closed my eyes.

"KIM! KIM!" It was Bob!

I opened my eyes to see him standing over me, again. "NO, you aren't real, you're a dream!"

Again, that horrible laugh, "Girl, you're dreaming about being married. That's what's not real. Now, GET OUT'TA THAT DAMNED BED!!!" His temper began to flare. His eyes ablaze with anger and impatience.

I sat bolt upright with a gasp, to find myself in my room with Tom wrapped in the blanket with his head covered up. I reached over to touch him. "Yes, it's him, he is not a dream or a figment of my imagination. "He's real, this is real," I told myself, "THIS is real"

I settled back down,

"Girl, THAT was the dream," It was Bob in my face, mocking me "Girl, you are HERE with me! You ain't never gonna leave,"

"NO, NO, NO!" I screamed.

"Oh yes", he laughed that horribly evil laugh and as he told me I was never going to get married or have children, I was going to be turning tricks until the day I die...then he laughed again.

My eyes opened to find myself in my own bed, 2:00 in the morning, no Bob, Tom was next to me. Am I dreaming? Am I awake? How can I know? Putting my arm around Tom, I squeezed up close, but I couldn't tell, I couldn't tell. Tears began to stream down! I felt the tickle of droplets roll over the bridge of my nose, gravity pulling them down to the sheet under my head.

I didn't know which is real. Tom, felt real, but is he? Is he? Is he...!

Chapter 25

So many stories about prostitution seem to end with the same, "wish it was, ending". She decides to go home to her family, she says goodbye to the other girls and/or the person who helped her get out, she is dressed in very "square" clothing and she rides off into the sunset on a bus to live happily ever after.

Then there are the stories that glamorize a crime that can only implode on your life.

Unfortunately, getting away does not end like a fairy tale. It takes secrecy, strength and conviction to get away then past the memories, the fear, and getting through the nightmares. You may need therapy, medication for the depression and a willingness to forgive and move on. None of which can be done without the one that went through it with you, God.

When Kim had lost all faith in everyone and everything, she could have accepted what appeared as her only way out. Death. Just like so many ladies do. Kim could have allowed herself to stay in that false state of being she fell into. She could have become angry, venomous, or she could have traveled down any other number of destructive avenues, but she didn't. She was strong, God gave her that strength all she had to do is take hold and not give in.

No matter what you are going through or what you believe or don't believe, you are strong enough to get through it. Kim's plan took one year to get out, it took her living a lie, but then she spent three years living a lie. It just took knowing who she needed to play.

Bob drove across a number of states intent on revenge, he had a friend with him which meant there was trouble.

When they got to the house, no one was home. Kim's family had all gone to see relatives for a long weekend. Not knowing this, Bob and his friend began looking in the windows. As they were going from window to window, a neighbor happened to see them. He went out to confront these two men that drove a fancy car with Illinois license plates.

"Can I help you?"

Bob said they were friends of the family and were wondering where we were. The neighbor wasn't about to say anything other than "They are out."

Then Bob said, "I've forgotten the name of the school the kids go to, would you happen to know?"

His answer would stop them in their tracks and send them running back to Chicago. "I don't think that is any of your business and now maybe you can tell me what your true business is with this family. I am the Sheriff in town." The conscientious neighbor, by chance or design, was the town Sheriff.

The LORD is the stronghold of my life-- of whom shall I be afraid? When evil men advance against me to devour my flesh, when my enemies and my foes attack me, they will stumble and fall

Psalm 27:1

"Leaving that life behind was only the first step in my healing. I spent years looking behind me. I went through years of therapy, horrible nightmares, a broken marriage and many years of depression, anxiety and unwarranted guilt. But I am a survivor and now...now I remember God and I remember His Love for *even* me."

August 15, 2017-Kim-

"...neither height nor depth, nor anything else in all creation, will be able to separate us from the love of God that is in Christ Jesus our Lord."

Romans 8:39

Made in the USA
Columbia, SC
01 May 2021

36551245R00114